C000089963

ISBN 978-0-243-92662-6
PIBN 10734038

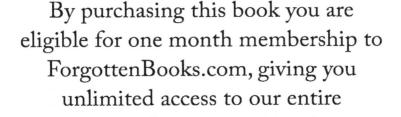

Vom

alten Mathematiker

Conrad Dasypodius.

Ein literarischer Versuch

der

Königlichen Societät der Wissenschaften zu
Göttingen im September 1794. vorgelegt,

von

Johann Georg Ludolph Blumhof.

Mit einer Vorrede

des

Herrn Hofraths *Kästner*.

Göttingen,
bey Johann Christian Daniel Schneider.
1796.

Nulla dies unquam memori vos eximet aevo.

14

Der
Königlichen Societät
der
Wissenschaften
zu
Göttingen

ehrfurcht- und hochachtungsvoll

gewidmet

vom Verfasser.

Vorrede.

Wem auch Dasypod nicht ganz unbekannt ist, der wird doch schwerlich soviel Arbeiten von ihm zu nennen wissen, als Herr Blumhof aufgefunden hat: Mehr als hundert Jahr nach Dasypods Tode, mufste eine Universität gestiftet werden, deren Büchersammlung, dem forschenden Freunde der Literatur, Urkunden aufbewahrte, die für soviel Mathematiker verschwunden waren.

Ein Beyspiel aus unzählichen, dafs der Gelehrte sich schmeichelt für die Nachwelt zu schreiben, und nur für die Vergessenheit schreibt.

Die Sittenlehre aus diesem so gewöhnlichen Schicksaale ist: Nächst dem Vergnügen das Beschäftigung mit den Wissenschaften ihrem Kenner allemahl gewährt, Erfüllung seiner Pflicht zum Hauptzwecke seiner Bemühung zu machen, und sich zu befriedigen daſs sie in dem Zusammenhange der Dinge Nutzen bringe wenn auch, der sie unternahm, für die Nachwelt ein Anonymus würde.

Daſs Strasburg seit Dasypods Zeiten immer geschickte Mathematikverständige gehabt hat, ist sicher, erst unmittelbare dann mittelbare, Folge seiner Arbeiten.

Dasypod empfohl Mathematik von den Griechen zu lernen, und hinderte dadurch ohne Zweifel, zu groſse Verbreitung, von Ramus gut gemeynten, aber sehr unglücklich ausgefallenen, Verbesserungen der Methode. Vor der Übersetzung der sphärischen Lehren, XVII in Hrn. Blumhof Verzeichnisse, steht: D. Petro Ramo Viro singulari Eruditione praedito, amico suo veteri Cunradus Dasypodius S. D.

D. erzählt er habe in einer Versammlung griechischer Philosophen und Mathematiker zugehört, dabey sich auch Peurbach, Regiomontan, Copernicus, Commandinus, befunden. Man habe über die Wiederherstellung der mathematischen Wissenschaften gesprochen. Euklid und

Archi-

Archimed haben behauptet, die Elemente müssten zuerst gelernt werden, wenn man nicht in ganz ungeometrisches Wesen verfallen wollte, Ptolemäus habe dargestellt wie Astronomie auf Beobachtungen und Beweisen beruhe, Heron von Alexandrien habe sich beschwert dass seine Schriften vernachlässigt würden, in denen er die Theorie zur Ausübung angewandt habe.... Entschieden habe man nichts, Dasypod aber glaubt, wenn ein Spruch erfolgen sollte, würde der seyn: Dass viele Werke der Neuern den Vorschriften dieser Philosophen und Mathematiker nicht gemäss sind, weil sie weder Beweise noch mathematische Ordnung haben. Zunächst verspricht Dasypod, ausführlich zu melden was er von des Ramus Scholis mathematicis halte. Das Schreiben d. 4. Dec. 1571. zu Strasburg.

Ich vermuthe nicht dass Dasypod sein Versprechen gehalten hat. Es war wohl kaum im Ernste gethan. Denn was er von des Ramus Behandlung der Mathematik hielt, hatte er schon in die Erzählung eingekleidet.

Dasypod veranlaßte der Griechischen Mathematiker Lehren, sich in ihrer Sprache bekannt zu machen. Dadurch beförderte er auch philologische Kenntnisse. So hatte er Beyfall und Unterstützung Johann Sturms, dessen Unterricht, griechische und lateinische Gelehrsamkeit in Deutschland so sehr beförderte.

Er lieferte von vielen alten Schriftstellern, nur die Sätze, ohne Beweise, selbst ohne Figuren. Deßwegen rechtfertiget er sich in einem Schreiben an den Kais. Leibarzt Joh. Crato von Kraftheim 1571. datirt, das sich vor dem griechischen Abdrucke nur erwähnter sphärischer Schriftsteller befindet. Er habe auf dieser Ausgabe nur Nebenstunden wenden können, und der Drucker habe zur vollständigen Lieferung nicht Zeit gehabt.

Dieses war wohl dem Aufwande gemäß den Anfänger bey Lehrbüchern machen konnten; Er ergänzte es durch mündlichen Unterricht, und immer befriedigte man sich in jenen Zeiten schon damit, zu wissen was die Alten gelehrt hatten.

Eigent-

Eigentlich waren auch diese Handbücher nur Proben einer Sammlung griechischer Mathematiker, die so vollständig als möglich werden sollte. In eben der Ausgabe sphärischer Schriften, findet sich vor dem griechischen Abdrucke von des Mönchs Barlaam astronomischer Logistik ein Schreiben Andreae Duditio Sbardellato, darinn Dasypod meldet, was er zu dieser Sammlung schon besitze, und was er noch ferner zu haben wünsche.

Eine ähnliche Unternehmung hatte Edward Bernard. Die zeigt bey der sehr seltenen Vita Edwardi Bernardi ... Scriptore Thoma Smitho. ... Lond. 1704. Veterum Mathematicorum Graecorum Latinorum et Arabum Synopsis collectore Edwardo Bernardo.

Zu Bernards Zeiten ... er starb 1696. ... war von den griechischen Mathematikern mehr bekannt. Er wollte ihnen Übersetzer, Commentatoren, Neuere welche eben die Gegenstände bearbeitet hatten, u. s. w. beyfügen; Dieses mit den Lateinern und Arabern, auch syrischer und arabischer Ue-

 ber-

bersetzung von Schriften die in der Grundsprache nicht zu finden sind, sollte XIV Bände ausmachen, versteht sich in Folio.

Zu dieser Sammlung fanden sich in Bibliotheken die Materialien, die Dasypod für die seinige noch suchte. Sie ist aber auch nicht erschienen, obgleich damahls noch die Zeit der Folianten war, wie jezo die Zeit der Almanache in klein Octav und Duodez.

Dasypod war nicht Erfinder, nur Herausgeber, Erläuterer, und Sammler, in seinen Compendien (VIII; IX.) und Lexicon (XVIII). Auch bey dem Baue der Uhr (XXV) hat er wohl nur, bekannte theoretische Lehren durch Handarbeit sinnlich dargestellt.

Seine schriftstellerischen Bemühungen verbreiteten Wahrheiten, und bildeten Mathematiker; Sein Kunstwerk belehrte und ergötzte seine Mitbürger, ward unter Strasburgs Merkwürdigkeiten genannt, wie der Thurm.

In der Mathematik haben die Vorfahren sichere Lehren hinterlassen, deren Anwenwendung schon Verdienst ist, wenn man ihnen auch nichts zusetzt.

Und blos dadurch daſs man Wahrheiten entdeckt, die den Alten noch nicht bekannt waren, erlangt man den Ruhm was Neues geleistet zu haben.

Anders, als bey Philosophen, wo was Neues leisten heiſst: das Alte für falsch und unbrauchbar erklären.

So gehn die Mathematiker immer weiter fort, und manche Philosophen fangen immer von vorne an.

Eine groſse Ursache von diesem Unterschiede ist: daſs die mathematische Kunstsprache so deutlich bestimmt, und so beständig ist. Käme Euklid wiederum auf die Welt, und lernte französisch oder deutsch, so verstände er jeden französischen oder deutschen Schriftsteller von der Elementargeometrie, unsere Rechnung mit Zifern und Buchstaben wäre das einzige ihm fremde, und die würde ihm bald bekannt werden. Manchen Beweisen, würde er freilich seinen Beyfall nicht geben.

Aber

Aber jezige deutsche Philosophen, und jezige deutsche Philosophen, verstehen ja einander nicht.

So erhob sich der Palast der Mathematik, von dem Euklids Elemente das unterste Stockwerk sind; Und den Philosophen, die immer neue Sprachen reden, ging es, wie den Bauleuten in der Ebene des Landes Sinear.

Göttingen; im December 1795.

Abraham Gotthelf Kästner.

Ich

Ich wage es, hier einige Nachrichten, oder vielmehr Fragmente von dem Leben und Schriften eines alten, schon beynahe in Vergessenheit gekommenen, aber gewiſs sehr verdienstvollen Mathematikverständigen vorzulegen, von dessen Lebensumständen zwar wenig bekannt ist, — der es aber doch in jeder Rücksicht verdient, daſs man sein Andenken erneure. Dieser Mann war ein Deutscher, und zugleich ein Beweis, daſs es unter der deutschen Nation von jeher groſse Geister und verdienstvolle Männer gegeben habe. Zur Ehre Deutschlands muſs ich es sagen, daſs aus seinem Schooſse die gröſsten Philosophen und Mathematiker gröſstentheils hervorkamen. *Keppler, Leibnitz, Thomasius, Wolf,* — und welch' eine Menge deutscher Genies, die als ewige Sternbilder am Himmel der Wissenschaften glänzen! — Und wie viele giebt es nicht, deren Werke, als eine Folge des Fanatismus und der Vorurtheile jener dunklen Zeiten, worin sie lebten, entweder verloren gegangen, oder bloſs in gelehrten Rüstkammern, im Staube begraben, das Schicksal der Vergänglichkeit aller menschlichen Dinge erfahren müssen? Oft war ihr Wirkungskreis zu beschränkt, ihre Einkünfte zu klein und ihre übrigen Vermögensumstände zu miſslich, als daſs sie hätten mehr thun, und mit ihren Talenten der Welt mehr nützen können! Und wem fallen hier nicht die Worte unsers verehrungswürdigen Herrn

Herrn Hofrath *Kästners a)* ein, da er Deutschlands Undankbarkeit gegen Verdienste rügt: «Deutschland, sagt er, diese »fruchtbare aber nachläſsige Mutter groſser »Geister, lieſs Kepplern mit Armuth und »Elend streiten, eben da er im Begrif war, »den himmlischen Körpern Gesetze vorzu»schreiben! Undankbares Vaterland, wä»rest du wohl eines Newtons würdig gewe»sen?»

«Wahrheit war die Botschaft die alle gro»ſsen Männer an die Menschheit zu verkündi»gen hatten. Wahrheit, Verhältniſs der »Dinge unter einander und zu uns. Sie ent»ledigten sich getreu ihres Auftrages, und »brachten uns Wahrheit, das Kleinod dem »Weisen, das Schwerd in eines Narren Hand. »Doch Nutzen und Miſsbrauch haben ihre »Gränzen; die Aufklärung aber schreitet von »Erfahrung zu Erfahrung ins Unbegränzte »fort. — — Wie schmeichelhaft ist für »jeden der es fassen kann, das Gefühl von »der Würde des menschlichen Geistes, bei »jeder groſsen und glücklichen Anstrengung »seiner Kräfte! Wer fühlt sich nicht groſs, »wenn er mit den Sternkundigen die unge»meſsenen Räume des Weltalls auf Flügeln »der Gedanken durchirrt! In der That, »wie bewundernswürdig ist nicht der mensch»liche Verstand, wenn er Mittel ersinnt, die »Entfernungen und Gröſse der Sonne genau »zu bestimmen, wenn er neue Planeten und »Cometen entdeckt, die dem bloſsen Auge uner-

a) In seiner Lobrede auf die Sternkunst.

»unerreichbar sind, und dennoch ihre Bah-»nen berechnet, als wären sie sichtbar! In »welchem erhabenen Lichte erscheinet nicht »jene stolze Wissenschaft, welche aus dem »Wenigen, was sie von der Erfahrung ent-»lehnt, die wichtigsten Folgerungen zieht, »wenn eine bemerkte Verschiedenheit in »dem Abstande gewisser Fixsterne von einan-»der, die gleichwohl kaum in Jahrtausenden »dem blofsen Auge auffallend werden könn-»ten, dem Scharfsinn des Mefskünstlers hin-»reichend ist, um eine progressive Bewegung »des ganzen Sonnensystems daraus nicht »blofs zu *muthmafsen*, sondern darzuthun, »und dann tausend neue Welten in jenen »entfernten Nebelpünktchen des allumfassen-»den Aethers zu erblicken *b*)!»

Wenn wir aber auch hingegen von den Lebensumständen berühmter Gelehrten, Schriftsteller und Künstler oft nur wenig, und das Wenige noch dazu sehr unzuverläfsig wissen; wenn kein gleichzeitiger Biograph uns ihre Geschichte aufgezeichnet, vielmehr in Gelehrten-Lexicis blofs die Titel von ihren Schriften verewigt sind: so sind doch oft die Werke und Arbeiten solcher Menschen, noch nach Jahrhunderten, und weiter hinaus, redende Beweise ihrer vortreflichen Kenntnisse und ihres Scharfsinns. Und eben dieses ist, glaub' ich, Ursache und Antrieb genug, solche Werke und ihre Meister der Vergessenheit zu entreifsen, und wenigstens diejenigen Nachrichten zu sammeln, die hin und wie-

b) *Georg Forster in Coo'ks* Denkmal. S. 18. 18.

wieder zerstreut sind. Ich werde hier vom *Conrad Dasypodius*, der im 16ten Jahrhundert in Strafsburg lebte, und ein Zeitgenosse vom *Daniel Spekle* war, einige Nachrichten vorlegen *):

Von *Dasypodii* Lebensumständen, ist meines Wissens keine ausführliche Nachricht vorhanden. In *Jöchers* Gelehrten-Lexicon findet man nur folgende kurze Nachricht: «Er hat verschiedene griechische Astrologos »z. B. Theodosium, Autolycum, und andre »zusammendrucken lassen, und einige Trak»tate von der Geometrie, Optik, Astrono»mie, als scholia et resolutiones s. tabulas in »*Claud. Ptolemaei* libros 4. apotelesmaticos; »in Aristotelis librum 1. meteorologicorum; »erotemata institutionum mathematicarum »cum appendice etc. geschrieben. — Er »starb den 26sten April 1600. im 68sten Jahre »seines Alters.» — —

So weit *Jöcher;* was ihn aber am meisten bei der Nachwelt verewigt, ist ohne Zweifel, die Erfindung des vormals so berühmten astronomischen Uhrwerks im Münster zu Strafsburg, welches sich noch daselbst befindet, aber nicht mehr geht. Von diesem wird unten bei Gelegenheit der von *Dasypodius* herausgegebenen eignen Beschreibung umständlicher geredet werden. *Dasypodius* dach-

*) Sein eigentlicher Name war *Rauhfufs*, weil es aber unter den Gelehrten damals Mode war, ihre Namen zu verändern, so änderte er seinen in *Dasypodius* um.

dachte auch schon darauf, die Werke aller alten Mathematiker nach und nach in einer Sammlung herauszugeben. Nur fehlte es ihm, wie es gemeiniglich bei solchen Sachen leider! der Fall ist — an hinlänglicher Unterstützung, und thätigen Mitarbeitern. Dieses Werk, wenn es zu Stande gekommen wäre, hätte gewiss in der mathematischen Litteratur Aufsehen gemacht, besonders da man weiss, wie wenig sonst Kenner und Liebhaber alter Sprachen, sich an die Bearbeitung alter mathematischer Schriftsteller geben.

Seine verschiedenen Schriften c) sind:

I) Euclidis Catoptrica, id est Elementa ejus scientiae, qua universa speculorumvit atque natura explicatur: primum Graece, antehac nunquam in lucem edita; et nunc nova translatione per *Conradum Dasypodium* in Latinam linguam translata. Argentorati. 1557. 4. 19 Blätter.

Catal. Bibl. Frobes. P. II. p. 191. *Heilbronner* Hist. Mathes. p. 160. *Scheibels* Einleitung zur mathematischen Bücherkenntniss 1 St. S. 12; 9 St. S. 266.

II*) ΕΥΚΛΕΙΔΟΥ ΤΩΝ ΠΕΝΤΕ ΚΑΙ ΔΕΚΑ ΣΤΟΙΧΕΙΩΝ, ΕΚ ΤΩΝ ΤΟΥ ΘΕΩΝΟΣ etc.

c) Diejenigen Schriften, welche ich selbst, theils aus Hrn. Hofr. *Kästners*, theils aus hiesiger Universitätsbibliothek in Händen gehabt, sind mit einen * bezeichnet.

etc. Euclidis quindecim Elementorum Geometriae primum ex Theonis Commentariis Graece et Latine. Cui accesserunt scholia, in quibus ad percipienda Geometriae Elementa spectant, breviter et dilucide explicantur, authore *Cunrado Dasypodio*, Scholae Argentinensis professore. Argentorati Excudebat Christianus Mylius. J564. 8. 4 Blätter; 189 Seiten.

Enthält bloss das 1ste Buch von Euklid's Elementen, mit der lateinischen Version bis p. 149. Hernach folgen die Erläuterungen bis p. 189.

III*) ΕΥΚΛΕΙΔΟΥ etc. Euclidis quindecim elementorum Geometriae secundum: ex Theonis commentariis Graece et Latine. Item Barlaam monachi Arithmetica demonstratio eorum quae in secundo libro elementorum sunt in lineis et figuris planis demonstrata. Item Octo propositiones stereometriae, ejusdem cum praecedentibus argumenti. Per *Cunradum Dasypodium* scholae Argentinensis Professorem. 8. 126 Seiten; 8 Blätter.

Enthält das zweite Buch von Euklid's Elementen griechisch und lateinisch, nebst des *Barlaam* (ein Mönch und Mathematiker aus den 15ten Jahrhundert,) Arithmetik, welche ein Kommentar desjenigen ist, was Euklid in seinem 2ten Buche auf Linien und ebne Figuren angewandt hat. Am Ende steht: Argentorati apud Christianum Mylium. 1564.

IIII*)

IIII*) Propositiones reliquorum Librorum Geometriae Euclidis, Graece, et Latine, in usum eorum, qui volumine Euclidis carent. Per *Cunradum Dasypodium*, scholae Argent. etc. Argentorati apud Christianum Mylium. 1564. 8. 205 Seiten. 8 Blätter.

Diese Schrift enthält die übrigen Bücher des Euklides, vom 3ten bis inkl. des 13ten, griechisch und lateinisch.

V) *Christiani Herlini* et *Cunradi Dasypodii* Euclideae Demonstrationes in Syllogismos resolutae. Argentorati. 1564. fol.

Heilbronner Hist. Mathes. p. 160. n. 19. *Scheibel* l. c. St. 5. S. 462.

VI*) Analyseis geometricae sex librorum Euclidis. Primi et quinti factae a *Christiano Herlino*: reliquae una cum Commentariis, et Scholiis perbrevibus in eosdem sex libros Geometricos. a *Cunrado Dasypodio*. Pro schola Argentinensi. Arg. 1566. fol. zweite Ausgabe. Ebend. 1571. fol.

Ein Kommentar über die 6 ersten Bücher der Elemente des Euklid's. Das 1te u. fünfte, ist eine Arbeit des Prof. Herlin, wie der Titel sagt, die andern aber sind, nebst den erläuternden Anmerkungen vom Dasypodius. Man findet da die Beweise in förmliche Schlüsse zerlegt, und durch die Verbindung derselben, wird Anfängern gezeigt, wie ein Beweis nach aller logischen Schärfe daraus entstehe. Das ganze Buch enthält XCVIII und V Folioblätter;

VII) *Dasypodii* Logistica. Argent. 1567. 8.
Heilbronner etc. p. 796. *Scheibel* etc. 11 St. S. 36.

VIII) Volumen primum mathematicum. Prima et simplicissima Mathematicarum disciplinarum principia complectens: Geometriae. Logisticae. Astronomiae. Geographiae. Per *Cunradum Dasypodium* in utilitatem Academiae Argentinensis collectum. Una cum Classium ejusdem Academiae, ordinariis Lectionibus. Arg. excudebat. *Josias Risselius*. 1567. 8.
Scheibel etc. 15 St. S. 49. 50.

IX) Compendium Theoriae Planetarum.
Vom Hrn. Prof. *Kall* als eine, besonders 1567. zu Strafsburg herausgekommene Schrift angemerkt. *Scheibel* l. c.

X) Hypotyposes orbium coelestium congruentes cum tabulis Alfonsinis et Copernici, seu etiam tabulis Prutenicis, editae à *Cunrado Dasypodio*. Argent. 1568. 8.
Bibl. Thuana. P. II. p. 68. *Scheibel* etc. 15. St. S. 52.

XI) Euclidis Propositiones. Elementorum. 15. Catoptricorum. Opticorum. Harmonicorum. Et Apparentiarum. Per *Cunradum Dasypodium*. Arg. Apud haeredes Christiani Mylii. 1570. 8. Titel, Zuschrift, Vorrede 7 Bl.; Text 81 Bl. und Übersetzung 87 Blätter.
Scheibel etc. 5 St. S. 463.

XII) De terminis geometricis per *Dasypodium* Arg. 1570.
Scheibel etc. 6 St. S. 658.

XIII)

XIII) Euclidis Elementorum Liber primus. Item, Heronis Alexandrini vocabula quaedam geometrica: ante hac nunquam edita, graece et latine. Per M. *Cunradum Dasypodium.* Cum gratia et privilegio Caesareo, atque Regis Galliae, ad sexennium. Argentinae 1571. 8. 50 Bl. Text. Übersetzung 21. und 8 Blätter.

Scheibel etc. 1 St. S. 18.

XIV) Euclidis varia Scripta Graece et Latine, edita a *Cunrado Dasypodio.* Argent. 1571. 8.

Fabricius Bibl. Graec. p. 377. 378. 380. *Scheibel* etc. 1 St. S. 18.

XV) Euclidis omnes omnium Librorum Propositiones graece et latine: editae per M. *Cunradum Dasypodium.* Cum gratia etc. . . Arg. 1571. 8. Text 93 Blätter, Übers. 98. u. 8 Blätter.

Ist einerlei mit obiger Ausgabe. *Scheibel* etc. 5 St. S. 463.

XVI) Euclidis Phaenomena in Sphaericis scriptoribus *Cunradi Dasypodii.* Argent. 1572. 8.

Bose in Jobelaeo astron. seculi ineuntis quarti. (Vitemb. 1759. 4.) p. 60. not. 53. 54. *Scheibel* etc. 1 St. S. 18.

XVII*) Sphaericae Doctrinae Propositiones Graece et Latine, nunc primum per M. *Cunradum Dasypodium,* in lucem editae, quorum authores sequens indicat pagina. Cum privilegio Caesareae Majestatis ad sexennium

 et

et Regis Galliae ad septennium. Excudebat Christianus Mylius. Argentorati. 1572. 8.

Nach der Dedication und Vorrede folgen zuerst *Theodosii* 3 Bücher de Sphaera; ferner dessen Buch de habitationibus und endlich dessen 2 Bücher de diebus et noctibus. Ferner *Autolyci* Buch de Sphaera mobili; 2 Bücher de Ortu et Occasu stellarum und endlich *Euklid's* Phaenomena bis p. 61. Hierauf folgen, mit einem besondern Titel: Propositiones Logisticae Astronomicae *Barlaami* Monachi Lib. sex. graec. 39 paginae, hernach die lateinische Übersetzung aller dieser Schriften auf 64. u. 47 Seiten.

XVIII*) ΛΕΞΙΚΟΝ, seu Dictionarium Mathematicum, in quo Definitiones et Divisiones continentur scientiarum Mathematicarum, . . . M. *Cunrado Dasypodio* Authore. Argent. 1573. 8. griechisch und lateinisch.

Dieses Buch enthält die vornehmsten Kunstwörter, welche in der Arithmetik, Geometrie, Geodäsie, Astronomie und Musik vorkommen, auf eine leichte und faſsliche Art erklärt, und konnte den Anfängern zu einer Art von mathematischen Encyclopädie dienen.

XIX) Euclidis Elementa Graece et Latine. Interpr. *Cunrado Dasypodio*, cum Scholiis. Argent. 1573. 8.

Scheibel etc. 1 St. S. 19.

XX) *Cunradi Dasypodii*, Mathematici Argent. Scholia et Resolutiones seu Tabulae in Lib. III, Apotelesmaticos *Cl. Ptolemaei*:

Una

Una cum Aphorismis eorundem Librorum. Denique brevis explicatio Astronomici Horologii Argentoratensis, ad veri et exacti temporis investigationem extracti.

Steht in folgenden äusserst seltenen Buche: *Hieronymi Cardani*, in Cl. Ptolemaei de Astrorum Judiciis, aut (ut vulgo appellant), Quadripartitae Constructionis Lib. IIII. Commentaria, ab Authore postremum castigata, et locupletata. His accesserunt, ejusdem *Cardani*, de septem erraticarum stellarum qualitatibus atque viribus liber posthumus, ante non visus. Geniturarum item XII. ad hanc scientiam recte exercendum observatu utilium exempla etc.. . . Basileae ex Officinae Henricpetrina. 1578. fol. Hr. Prof. *Scheibel* (Mathem. Bücherk. 16 St. S. 100.) bemerkt, dass er die Beschreibung der Strassburger Uhr in seinem Exemplare vermisse, obgleich der Titel darauf aufmerksam macht. Diese steht aber auch in der Schrift n. XXV.

XXI*) Brevis doctrina de Cometis, et Cometarum effectibus, Per M. *Cunradum Dasypodium*. (Argentor. Excudebat N. Wyriot.) 1578. 4. 5. Bogen.

XXII*) *Von Cometen, vnd jhrer würkung. durch M. Cunradum Dasypodium beschriben. Gedruckt zu Strassburg* bey *Niclauss Wyriot*. 1578. 4. 4½ Bogen.

Diese beiden Abhandlungen enthalten nichts besonders. Man sieht vielmehr daraus, dass ein Prof. der Mathematik im 16ten Jahrhundert ziemlich verwirrte Begriffe von diesen Schweifsternen hatte.

XXIII) Isaaci Monachi Scholia in Euclidis Elem. VI. priores libros, per *Dasypodium*. Argent. 1579. 8.

Fabricius. p. 374. *Scheibel* etc. 1 St. S. 21.

XXIIII*) Oratio *Cunradi Dasypodii* de disciplinis Mathematicis: Ad Fridericum II. Sereniss. Regem Daniae etc. *Ejusdem* Hieronis Alexandrini nomenclaturae Vocabulorum Geometricorum translatio. *Ejusdem* Lexicon Mathematicum, ex diversis collectum antiquis scriptis. Excudebat Nicolaus Wyriot. Argent. 1579. 8.

In der Oratio giebt *D.* zuförderst einige allgemeine Nachrichten von dem Zustande der mathematischen Disciplinen unter den Alten. Bei den Babyloniern und Chaldäern waren die mathematischen Wissenschaften in grofsem Ansehen. In Indien brachten Gymnosophisten, in Ägypten die Sacerdotes, in Griechenland Mathematici, Dichter und Philosophen und bei den Juden die Propheten, die Wissenschaften in Aufnahme. — Thales Milesius lebte vor Christi Geburt 584. unter den Sacerdoten in Ägypten, und bereicherte nachher unter den Griechen die Mathematik mit treflichen Erfindungen. — Etwas weniges vom Pythagoras und seinen Nachfolgern, und den Fortgange dieser Wissenschaft unter den Griechen. — *Hieron Alexandrini* Nomenmenclaturae Voc. Geometric. verdienen, wegen ihrer Deutlickeit und gedrungener Kürze gelesen zu werden. Vom Ursprung der Geometrie z. B. sagt er folgendes: Inventa est Geometria primum ab Aegyptiis, Thales postea in graeciam eam transtulit: et post Thaletem, Mamertius frater Stesichori poetae et Hippias Eleus. post hosce Pythagoras, paulo latius considerans hujus scientiae principia: et inquirens theoremata sine materia, et mente solum concepta. Post hunc Anaxagoras, et Plato, et Oenopides Chius, Theodorus Cyraenaeus, et ante Platonem, Hippocrates, post hunc Leodamas Thasius, et Architas Tarentinus, Theaetetus Atheniensis, Eudoxus Knidius qui tribus proportionibus, alias tres adjecit: et multi alii sed his non multo est junior Euclides qui Elementa conscripsit. fuit autem tempore primi Ptolemaei junior Platone: major vero natu Eratosthene, et Archimede, hi enim uno eodemque vixerunt tempore. — Bl. 18. — Hin und wieder hat *D.* den Grundtext verbessert und erläutert. Diese Übersetzung enthält 31 Blätter. Das mathematische Lexicon ist mit obigem einerlei; es ist nur ein neuer Abdruck lateinisch und griechisch. 47 und 44 Blätter. Am Ende steht: Argentorati Excudebat Nicolaus Wyriot. Anno 1573.

XXV*) *C. Dasypodii* **Heron Mechanicus:** Seu de Mechanicis artibus, atque disciplinis.

 Ejus-

Ejusdem Horologii astronomici, Argentorati in summo Templo erecti, descriptio. Argent. Excudebat Nicolaus Wyriot. 1580. 4.

Zuerst über den Zustand der mechanischen Künste und Wissenschaften bei den Alten. Hierauf die Beschreibung des Astronomischen Uhrwerks zu Strafsburg. *D.* bekam 1570. vom Magistrat der Stadt Strafsburg den Auftrag, einen Plan zu einem Uhrwerke zu entwerfen, welches alle bisherige an Kunst und Pracht übertreffen sollte, denn die alte Uhr in der Cathedralkirche, war durch die Länge der Zeit unbrauchbar geworden. Er entwarf einen Plan, welcher auch unter seiner Aufsicht 1571. angefangen und erst 1574. vollendet wurde *d*). Das Ganze

d) Mehrere Nachrichten, als die hier aus des *Dasypodii* Buche beigefügte kurze Beschreibung, findet man in *Jac. von Königshoven* Elsafs. und Strafsb. Chronik. herausgegeben von *Schiltern*. S. 574. f. — L'Histoire d'Alsace du P. *Laguille*. T. I. P. II. p. 255. — *J. Schweighäuser* Description nouvelle de la Cathedrale de Strafsbourg, et de sa fameuse Tour. . . . avec Fig. 3e Ed. à Strafsb. 1770. 8. p. 71. Kurz nach ihrer Vollendung erschien: Carmen de astronomico Horologio Argentoratensi, scriptum à M. *Nicodemo Frischlino*, Balingens. Acad. Tub. Prof. Item de eodem schediasma *Guil Xylandri* etc.. . . Arg. 1575. 4. Man findet hier eine poetische Beschreibung aller Theile dieser Uhr, und Nachrichten von den vornehmsten Künstlern, die daran gearbeitet haben. Hinten steht noch ein anderes ze ist mit einem Gitterwerk umgeben und in 3 Abtheilungen gebracht. Am Fuſse desselben ist ein Globus, welcher auf den Rücken eines Pelikans ruht; er hat 3 Fuſs im Durchmesser, und sein Gewicht ist 100 Pfund. Die Composition dazu ist Kütt, Kreide und Papier, um das Ganze recht fest zusammen zu halten. Man findet darauf 48 Konstellationen gemahlt, und vermittelst künstlicher, im Innern des Pelikans angebrachter Maschinerien vollenden Sonne, Mond und die übrigen Sterne ihre Umdrehungen. Diesem Globus gegenüber sind 3 Räder angebracht, davon das gröſste einen Kalender vorstellt; Apollo und Diana auf beiden Seiten, rücken die Tage und Nächte fort, und dieses Rad kömmt gerade alle Jahr einmahl herum e). Das mittlere Rad zeigt die güldene Zahl, Sonntagsbuchstaben, die beweglichen Feste und die Schaltjahre. Es kömmt in 100 Jahren nur einmal herum. Das dritte und

res Lobgedicht von *Wilh. Xylander*, welches er schediasma nennt, nebst einem Briefe desselben an *Dasypodius* vom 4ten Sept. 1574.

e) Stant gemini circum, proles Latonia Phoebus,
Et Phoebi Diana soror: praesignis uterque
Virgineo vultu et telis clypeoque decoro.
Hinc atque hinc pictus telo de parte sinistra
Orbis, Apollo diem quemvis toto indicat anno.
Oppositam digito Phoebe notat aurea noctem
Indice: quae medium post annum tarda sequetur.
Frischlin. Carmen in Horolog.

und kleinste Rad ist unbeweglich; es enthält ausser der Karte von Deutschland und dem Plan von Strasburg, auch die Namen derer die an diesem Werke gearbeitet haben. An den 4 Ecken dieser Scheibe sind die 4 Monarchien der Welt beschrieben, und auf zwo andern Seiten sind auf zwei grossen Tafeln, die Sonn- und Mondfinsternisse von 1575. bis 1605. vorgestellt. — Unmittelbar über diesen Maschinen befinden sich die 7 Planeten, in Figuren, jede auf einen Wagen sitzend, welche von ihnen geweiheten Thieren gezogen werden. Sie erscheinen eins ums andre, jeder an dem Tage, welcher nach ihm genennet wird. Die Namen der Tage findet man in folgender Ordnung aufgeschrieben:

Sonntag, Apollo, oder die Sonne.	*dies Solis.*
Montag, der Mond.	*dies Lunae.*
Dienstag, Mars.	*dies Martis.*
Mittwochen, Merkur.	*dies Mercurii.*
Donnerstag, Jupiter.	*dies Jovis.*
Freitag, Venus.	*dies Veneris.*
Sonnabend, Saturn.	*dies Sabbati.*

Etwas höher sieht man die Scheibe, welche die Minuten und Viertelstunden anzeigt. Auf jeder Seite steht ein Engel, davon der eine bei jedem Stundenschlage seinen Scepter, den er in der Hand hält, aufhebt, während der andre seine Sanduhr umdreht. — In der zweiten Abtheilung befindet sich ein grosses Astrolabium, auf welchem sich verschiedene Nadeln oder Zeiger herumdrehen.

Der

Der größte kömmt alle 24 Stunden einmal herum und zeigt die Stunden; die andern stellen die Bewegungen der Planeten im Thierkreise, vor. Im Mittelpunkte befindet sich ein Globus terrestris, auf dessen vier Ecken, die vier Jahrszeiten gemahlt sind. Zwei Löwen halten auf beiden Seiten die Wappen der Stadt und der Direktoren der Kirche. Unter dem Astrolabio befindet sich ein kleiner Quadrant, welcher den Lauf und die Zeit des Mondes anzeigt. In der dritten Abtheilung sind die Cymbeln oder kleinen Glöckchen, die alle Viertelstunden, vermittelst vier geharnischter Menschenfiguren, so die vier Alter der Menschen vorstellen, gespielt werden. Noch etwas höher ist die kleine Stundenglocke angebracht. Hier steht auf der einen Seite eine Christusfigur, und auf der andern im Kontrast, der Tod, welcher bei jedem Viertel sich der Glocke nähert, um die Stunde schlagen zu lassen, aber durch die andre Figur daran verhindert wird. Ist indessen die Uhr so weit vorgerückt, daſs die Stunde vollschlägt, so geht die Menschenfigur zurück. Die Glocke hat folgende Inschrift: O Rex Gloriae Christe, veni cum pace. 1375. 3. Non. Augusti. Inwendig hängen noch verschiedene kleine Glocken, die durch ihr harmonisches Geläute, ein angenehmes Glockenspiel machen. — Der kleine Thurm zur Linken enthält die Gewichwichte der Uhr. Die Gemählde, welche seine Zierrathen ausmachen, sind von *Tobias Stimmer*. Oben auf steht ein Hahn, welcher nach Endigung des Glockenspiels mit den Flügeln zu schlagen anfängt und zweimal laut ruft. Etwas niedriger sieht man Uranien, als die Göttin der Mathematik; unter ihr einen Kolofs mit den 4 Monarchien, von denen beim Daniel Kap. 7. die Rede ist. Hiernächst das Bildnifs des berühmten Astronomen *Nicolaus Kopernikus*, welches *D.* aus Danzig geschickt bekam. Auf der linken Seite sieht man die 3 Göttinnen des menschlichen Lebens; Lachesis hält den Spinnrocken, Clotho spinnt und Atropos schneidet den Faden ab. *f*). Die Treppe, vermittelst welcher man zu dieser Uhr hinaufsteigt, ist auf der rechten Seite und eine der künstlichsten die es je geben kann. An dem Werke selbst haben 3 geschickte Meister, nemlich *Isaak*, *Abraham*, und *Josias Habrecht* gearbeitet.

Der von Zeit zu Zeit gemachten Reparaturen ungeachtet, verfällt das Werk doch immer mehr und mehr; indessen wird

f) Parte alia turris fatalia pensa trahentes
Considunt Parcae, quarum Dea ferrea, Clotho
Unque colum tenet: at Lachesis sub pollice fusum
Torquet, et humanam sortitur stamine vitam:
Atropos, instantis saevissima mortis imago,
Fila secat cultro, mortalesque abripit annos.
Frischlin. l. c.

wird es doch in der Geschichte der Erfindungen des menschlichen Geistes immer merkwürdig bleiben.

Das ganze Buch, ist ohne Seitenzahlen, und enthält 38 und 4 Quartblätter. Am Ende ist ein Verzeichniſs der Sonn- und Mondfinsternisse von 1575. bis 1605. angehängt.

XXVI*) *Cunradi Dasypodii* Protheoria mathematica, in qua non solum disciplinae Mathematicae omnes, ordine convenienti enumerantur: verum etiam universalia Mathematica praecepta; explicantur. Arg. 1593. 8.

Dasypodius handelt in diesem Werke hauptsächlich von der mathematischen Methode und von den Eintheilungen der mathematischen Wissenschaften. Das Buch selbst ist rar; ich habe es aus Hrn. Hofr. *Kästners* Bibliothek vor mir gehabt.

XXVII*) *Cunradi Dasypodii* Institutionum Mathematicarum Voluminis primi Erotemata. Logisticae. Geometriae. Sphaere. Geographiae. Cum Privilegio Caesareo. Pro schola Argentinensis imprimebat *Josias Rihelius* 1593. 8. 223 Seiten 8 Blätter.

Das Buch ist in Fragen und Antworten abgefaſst, und die letztern so kurz wie möglich. Hin und wieder ist der Text durch eingedruckte Holzschnitte erläutert.

XXVIII*) *Cunradi Dasypodii* Institutionum Mathematicarum Voluminis primi Erotematum. Appendix. Elementorum. Arithmeticae.

CPSIA information can be obtained
at www.ICGtesting.com
Printed in the USA
BVHW060248061118
532207BV00025B/4076/P

The Bedlington Terrier

A Complete and Comprehensive Beginners Guide to: Buying, Owning, Health, Grooming, Training, Obedience, Understanding and Caring for Your Bedlington Terrier

Michael Stonewood

ISBN: 9781090632371

CONTENTS

INTRODUCTION

Before purchasing any pet it is important to understand that as a pet owner you are responsible for the care and wellbeing of your pet. It is important to try and learn as much as you can about the animal you are considering to keep as a pet to make sure that your lifestyle, household and financial status are suited to provide your pet with the best possible care. This guide has been designed to provide you with both precise and concise information about a Bedlington Terrier's basic needs to help you provide your pet with the best quality care practices. This guide will give an in-depth explanation on training your Bedlington Terrier, raising your Bedlington Terrier from a puppy, grooming, health care and everything in between!

DESCRIPTION

The Bedlington Terrier is a small breed of dog that is named after the small mining town of Bedlington, in Northumberland, in North East England. The Bedlington Terrier is also commonly known as the 'Rothbury Terrier,' the 'Rodbery Terrier' and the 'Rothbury's Lamb.' The breed was originally developed to hunt small vermin in mines. However in recent years the Bedlington Terrier has been used in dog races, dog sports, dog conformation shows, as a companion dog and as a general family pet. The breed is known to be extremely quick, athletic and capable of out swimming many water dog breeds. The breed has a unique coat which gives it a similar aesthetic appearance to a lamb. Their coats normally come in the following four colorations: white, liver, blue or sandy. The Bedlington Terrier is known to be affectionate, playful, friendly and incredibly loyal to their family unit. However, it is important to know that the Bedlington Terrier is a highly jealous breed and is not afraid of 'fighting' or attacking other dogs, or pets, that its owners are showing attention to.

Lifespan

A Bedlington Terrier will normally live to be between 12 and 14 years old. However it is not uncommon for a Bedlington Terrier to live to be as old as 16, providing that they do not develop any serious health issues.

Height and Weight

A fully grown Bedlington Terrier will normally stand between 15 to 16 inches (38 to 40 cm) tall at the shoulder. A healthy adult Bedlington Terrier will normally weigh between 17 to 23 pounds (7.7 to 10.5kg). It is important to note that the weight of a healthy Bedlington Terrier depends on how large the Bedlington Terrier is – taller Bedlington Terriers should weigh more.

BREED CHARACTERISTICS

The following section will give you a simplistic overview of the characteristics of a Bedlington Terrier. Our rating system is from 1 to 10 – with 1 being the lowest score and 10 being the highest.

- **Adaptability:** 8/10
- **Friendliness:** 10/10
- **Health:** 6/10
- **Ease of Grooming:** 1/10
- **Amount of Shedding:** 10/10
- **Trainability:** 8/10
- **Intelligence:** 10/10
- **Exercise Needed:** 8/10
- **Playfulness:** 10/10
- **Family Friendliness:** 10/10

WHY SHOULD YOU PURCHASE A DOG?

In the United States of America it is estimated that there are between 70 and 80 million pet dogs owned and over 40% of the county's households own a dog! As the statistic shows dogs are incredibly popular pets – but why? Any dog owner will happily tell you all the benefits and joys of owning a dog! The following section will outline 5 key benefits of owning a dog:

Companionship

Dogs are incredibly loyal and loving animals and make a great addition to any household. If you build a strong relationship with your pet they can transcend just being a pet and become a friend, or ever a member of your family! However your dog brings you companionship in other ways. You are more likely to interact with strangers while walking your dog than if you were walking alone. Owning a dog also allows you to go to dog parks and converse with other dog owners. If you walk your dog around your neighborhood on a regular basis, you may also develop a friendly relationship with your neighbors who own dogs as you are likely to pass each other several times a day.

Exercise

Owning a dog increases your chance of exercising due to the fact that you will need to play with and walk your dog. Taking your pet for frequent walks will decrease your chance of becoming over weight. A recent study in Australia found that children with a pet dog are 50% less likely to be overweight! Exercising on a regular basis has a plethora of other health benefits such as reducing the chance of heart disease, strokes and high blood pressure. A dog can be a great exercise companion as well as being a great motivation due to the fact that it is cruel to not provide your dog with adequate exercise.

Watchdog

Dogs are very territorial, loyal and aware as a species. Even from as early as puppyhood, a dog is able to detect potential burglars and dangers. Your dog will bark at anything suspicious or out of the ordinary which will alert you to any potential trouble. Most criminals are instantly put off by the barking of a watchdog.

Nurturing

The majority of humans have a deep desire to nurture. This desire used to be fulfilled by caring for, and raising, a baby or caring for younger siblings. Across the Western World the average family size is decreasing which makes pets the perfect outlet for people's nurturing desires. In families with no children, or one child, dogs are fulfilling the role of being substitute children and siblings! Dogs are intelligent beings and respond well to being nurtured which makes it a positive and rewarding experiences for both the owner and the pet. Dogs also seem to nurture children. Children who own a dog tend to have a high self-esteem and are more popular with their classmates!

Empathy

Dogs are incredibly empathetic animals! They will sense the mood of their owner and either attempt to provide comfort, through physical contact, or a distraction through a humorous playful act. It is not uncommon for dogs to bring their distressed owners their favorite toy as an attempt to cheer them up. Dogs have also saved their owners from countless dangers – such as house fires and burglaries.

Responsibility

Purchasing a dog is one of the best ways to teach young children about the concept of responsibility. If you purchase a dog for your family and allow a child to be involved with caring for the dog it will help them to develop selflessness and responsibility. A child can be tasked with simple care routines such as: changing the water in the dog's bowl, feeding the dog or giving the dog its treats during training. If your child is older, or already has a good understanding of responsibility, you can give them more complex care tasks such as: grooming the dog, training the dog or walking the dog. Older children can also be given the task of introducing their younger siblings to the process of playing with and caring for a new dog.

DOG EQUIPMENT BASICS AND ESSENTIALS

Before purchasing a Bedlington Terrier it is important to make sure that you have already purchased all the equipment you will need to provide your new Bedlington Terrier with the best possible care. Ensuring you have all the essential equipment before purchasing your pet is the best way to build a strong relationship with your pet and to keep it content, happy and healthy.

Collars and ID Tags

Purchasing a collar with an ID tag is arguably one of the most important things you can purchase for your Bedlington Terrier. The collar allows you to attach a leash to your Bedlington Terrier, which in turns allows you to take your pet for a walk which is essential to their health. There are a wide range of collars available to purchase made from multiple different materials and styles. It is important to take your dog's habits into account when purchasing a collar. For example if your dog regularly enjoys swimming it is not advisable to purchase a leather collar. It is also important to not purchase a thin collar! When you walk your Bedlington Terrier on a leash it may lunge, or pull, which will cause the collar to dig into its neck. The wider the collar is the wider the area the force from the lunge is spread over – basically wider collars are more comfortable! The ID tag allows for your pet to be easily identifiable and returned to you if they are ever lost! I recommend having your Bedlington Terrier's name and your home address on the ID tag. This will allow the person who finds your dog to keep it calm by using its familiar name and will know where to return your pet to.

Leashes and Harnesses

Purchasing a lead, or harness, is vital in ensuring your Bedlington Terrier remains healthy! Having a lead, or harness, allows for you to walk your pet and provide them with the exercise they need. Walking your pet also helps to create a strong bond and friendship between the two of you. There are a few differences between Leashes and Harnesses which will be explained below:

- **Leash:** Most dog owners will use a leash while walking their pet. Leashes ensure both comfort and safety when you take your dog out for a walk. It is important to buy a leash that extends to allow your dog to explore and move away from you at times. It is equally important to buy a sturdy leash that will allow you to keep control of your pet for the entirety of the walk.

- **Harness:** If you have a large, small, energetic or boisterous dog a harness may be a safer option. The harness is safer for these types of dogs as they will not feel discomfort from their collar when they pull against the leash. Purchasing a front-clip harness (that goes over the dog's chest) will allow you to have more control over your pet.

Bedding

Some owners allow their dogs to sleep in their beds or on their sofas. While this can definitely be a great way to build a strong relationship with your dog it is also important to purchase a suitable bed for your pet. By providing your pet with its own bed it will give your dog a place of its own to feel safe and secure. There is an overwhelmingly wide variety of dog beds available in pet stores and on the internet. I recommend adhering to the following criteria when purchasing a dog bed to ensure both practicality, safety, comfort and warmth.

- **Natural Materials:** It is important to make sure the dog bed you purchase is made of natural materials. Synthetic products, including fire retardant and stain-proof chemicals, may be harmful to your dog's health.

- **Removable Cover:** If you purchase a dog bed that has a removable cover it allows for you to regularly and easily clean your dog's bed. Keeping your pet's bedding clean is essential to keeping your pet healthy as it removes bacteria and any parasites that may have found their way into the bedding. Purchasing a bed with a removable cover also allows you to replace the cover if it keeps overly worn and ripped – replacing just the cover is a lot less expensive than replacing an entire bed!
- **Non-Skid Bottom:** When your dog dives into its bed you do not want it to slide across the floor as this could cause damage to your pet, the bed and the floor. Purchasing a bed with a non-skid bottom removes the chance of injury and damages.
- **Plan Ahead:** If you are buying a puppy it is important to remember that your puppy will grow! It is considered best practice to purchase a bed that is the correct size for an adult dog so it will not be out grown.

There are two main categories of beds that are suitable for dogs. It is important to watch your dog sleep so you have an idea of how its sleeping preferences and how it physically lies down. Choosing the correct bedding is vital to ensure your dog feels safe and secure at home. The two categories of bedding are as follows:

- **Round / Nest-Style Beds:** These beds are ideal for smaller dogs and larger dogs who like to curl up when they sleep.
- **Raised / Cushion / Futon Beds:** These beds are ideal for dogs who enjoy stretching themselves out when they sleep.

Food and Water Bowls

It is important to purchase a food bowl and a water bowl for your pet Bedlington Terrier. There are three main materials that are used to create these bowls: plastic, ceramic, stainless steel. The following section will outline the pros and cons of each material.

- **Plastic:** Plastic bowls are cheap, durable and long lasting. The only downside of a plastic bowl is that plastic can be toxic to dogs if ingested. If you notice your dog gnawing at its bowl you should replace it with either a ceramic or stainless steel bowl.
- **Ceramic:** Ceramic bowls are very stable and heavy which makes them a good choice if your dog pushes its bowl while it eats or

drinks. The main downside of using a ceramic bowl is that they are porous and will therefore need to be thoroughly cleaned on a daily basis.

- **Stainless Steel:** Stainless Steel bowls are recommended by vets and dog care experts. They are easy to clean, easy to sanitize, durable and inexpensive. Similar to when purchasing a dog bed, it is considered best practice to purchase a stainless steel bowl with a non-skid bottom to prevent the bowl from moving while your dog eats or drinks.

Worms, Ticks and Fleas

Part of your responsibility as a Bedlington Terrier owner is to control and kill the parasites that your Bedlington Terrier will definitely get at some point. Worms, Ticks and Fleas can cause serious discomfort and health issues if left unchecked. There are medicated collars and shampoos that help to minimize your Bedlington Terrier's chance of getting fleas and ticks. There are also medicines you can purchase to help prevent both external and internal parasites. It is considered best practice to take your pet to your local vet and ask for them to give you a prescription for medicines to control parasites.

Toys

Toys for your Bedlington Terrier are essential for so many different reasons! Toys can provide your pet with mental and physical stimulation which can also lead them to having less destructive behavior patterns – such as chewing up furniture! Chew toys can also have dental health benefits. Toys also allow you to build a strong and fun relationship with your pet. The following list details some of the most popular toys available on the market:

- **Chew Toys:** Chew toys can provide your dog with hours of solo fun and can also help your dog to develop a strong and healthy jaw. Before giving your dog a chew toy it is important to check that it is not too hard – an overly hard chew toy can have the opposite effect and damage your dog's jaw! A good rule of thumb is to bang the chew toy on your knee – if it hurts it is too hard for your dog's mouth! It is likewise important to make sure that your dog does not ingest any of the chew toy though as the plastic, or rubber, is toxic!
- **Tug Toys:** Tug toys are a very popular choice as they allow for you to actively play with your dog. It is important to not allow your dog to become aggressive while you play

with the tug toy! To avoid your dog becoming aggressive you should keep a positive and happy inflexion in your voice. The most popular choices for tug toys are ropes and squishy plastic bones.

- **Balls and Fetch Toys:** Balls and fetch toys are another great way to actively play with your pet. It is important to purchase fetch toys made of soft plastic so your dog will suffer no dental damage or physical pain (if they miss the catch and get hit by the toy). A good choice for fetch toys are ball, Frisbees, cuddly toys and squishy plastic sticks. Tennis balls are a common choice for fetch but are not actually a healthy choice of toy! The covering on Tennis balls can actually abrade the enamel on your dog's teeth which can lead to serious health, and dental, issues in later life.
- **Food-Dispensing Toys:** Food-dispensing toys are a great way to mentally stimulate your dog. They come in a variety of different styles and shapes. I recommended purchasing a ball or cube as it will also allow your dog to push the toy around which encourages physical activity as well.

Expanding your Collection

Dogs are incredibly intelligent beings and, like humans, have preferences when it comes to bedding, food and how they have fun. Once you have developed a good understanding of your new Bedlington Terrier's preferences I recommended taking these preferences into account when purchasing new equipment and food.

BASIC COST OF OWNING A DOG

Owning a dog obviously costs money – but how much money? The following section will provide you with the average cost of owning a dog to help you decide whether you are in the correct financial state and to help you budget for any unexpected bills! It is important to remember that on average, dogs live for between 8 and 18 years.

Initial costs

- **Purchase of Dog:** Most Bedlington Terrier breeds cost between $200 and $1500.
- **Microchip:** If your Bedlington Terrier has not been microchipped before purchase this will cost $50.
- **Lifetime Council Registration:** This costs $49 for desexed Bedlington Terriers and $182 for Bedlington Terriers who have not been desexed.

Basic Equipment

- **Dog Bed:** Dog beds normally cost between $20 and $200.
- **Brush:** Most brushes designed for grooming

cost around $20.

- **Food and Water bowls:** Each bowl costs are $20 and you will need a minimum of two – one for water and one for food.
- **Collar, Lead, Tags and Harnesses:** A complete set will normally cost between $50 and $200.
- **Toys:** Dogs need a range of toys. I recommend setting aside between $50 and $100 dollars to provide your dog with the enough toys.

Preventative Health Care

- **Vaccination:** Vaccinations cost between $50 and $120 depending on which ones you get. Your dog will need vaccine at 8, 12 and 16 weeks of age and then every 3 years after that.
- **Worm Tablets:** Tapeworm and Heartworm prevention tablets cost about $10 a month.
- **Fleas:** Most flea prevention cost around $10 a month.
- **Bi-annual Vet Check:** You will need to take your dog for a health check at the vet every 6 months. A general health checkup costs around $65.

Food

- **Basic Food Needs:** Basic food (kibble) will cost you around $1,200 a year.
- **Treats:** Treats are not essential but most owners enjoy giving them to their dogs. I recommend budgeting around $100 a year for dog treats.
- **Dental Chew Sticks:** Dental chew sticks are a great way to improve your dog's jaw strength and dental hygiene. I recommend budgeting around $100 a year for dental chew sticks.

Grooming

- **Shampoo and Conditioner:** Shampoo and conditioner will normally cost around $30 a year. It is not necessary to buy expensive brands of shampoo and condition – basic products designed for dogs will work perfectly fine.
- **Visit to the Groomer:** Groomers normally charge between $50 and $150. I recommend taking your dog to the groomers at least twice a year.

Training, Dog Care and Walking

- **Puppy Training:** Puppy training normally costs around $100 for a month long training course.
- **Advanced Training:** Most owners enjoy taking their dogs to obedience classes and advanced training. These services normally cost around $170 for a month long course.
- **Dog Walking:** Dog walking normally costs around $25 an hour (depending on where you live).
- **Daycare:** Daycare services normally cost around $50 a day.
- **Boarding:** I recommend budgeting around $300 a year on boarding services. Most boarding services will charge around $50 a day.

Other Expenses

While I would love to tell you that the expenses listed above are the only expense you will incur while owning a dog, it is far from the truth. Dogs, like small children, are energetic, curious and playful. This can lead your pet to causing unexpected damages to furniture, your home and your car. All puppies will at some point destroy something valuable. When introducing a new dog into your home, I highly suggest moving your valuables into a safe, and out of reach, place. For example, if you have a recently added a large dog breed to your home it might be worthwhile removing the expensive vase you have as a table center piece until you know your dog will not disturb it. Likewise, if you have recently added a small dog to your home it might be worthwhile ensuring there are no small holes for your dog to climb inside. You do not want a small dog to get stuck in a small hole and end up having to damage your property to rescue your pet. When it comes to new dogs, it is always better to air on the side of caution! Puppies are known to chew anything they can get their mouth around, this includes: your television remote, laptop chargers, the gear stick in your car and the list goes on and on. I urge you to take preventative measures and protect your valuable possessions while your new pet settles into your home.

PURCHASING YOUR NEW PET

There are multiple different ways to purchase a dog: from a breeder, from a pet store or from a rescue service. There are pros and cons of each method and they will be explained in the following section.

Breeders

When it comes to purchasing a Bedlington Terrier, breeders are unarguably the best method. A breeder will allow you to interact with your Bedlington Terrier before you purchase it. This will allow you to understand the Bedlington Terriers temperament and behavior as well as allowing you to inspect the Bedlington Terrier for any genetic defects. Breeders are normally a part of a registered service – such as The Kennel Club. By being a member of a registered organization it gives the breeder accountability and legitimacy. Breeders will be able to inform you of any issues with the Bedlington Terrier and how they have been socializing it. Breeders will also be able to tell you the exact birthdate of your new Bedlington Terrier. The only downside of breeders is the fact that they are more expensive than pet stores – however this should not be an issue when you are considering purchasing a Bedlington Terrier.

Pet Stores

Pet stores are a common choice when purchasing a new Bedlington Terrier – but I HIGHLY do not recommend purchasing a Bedlington Terrier from a pet store! Most pet stores purchase their Bedlington Terriers from puppy mills. Puppy mills are notorious for breeding and raising their Bedlington Terriers in terrible conditions which leads to both behavioral and health problems. Employees at the pet store will most likely not be able to provide you with specific information about a Bedlington Terrier – they are unlikely to know its exact date of birth and health background. The pedigree of a Bedlington Terrier from a pet store is also questionable. Pet stores have a terrible return policy! It is not uncommon for a new owner to not have fully considered every aspect of owning a Bedlington Terrier and they therefore return it. If you return a Bedlington Terrier to a breeder you can be assured that the Bedlington Terrier will lead a happy life. However, if you return a Bedlington Terrier to a pet store it will most likely be euthanized, if it has grown to be older than a puppy, due to the fact that it is unlikely to sell.

Rescue

If you are an experienced Bedlington Terrier owner you may considered getting a Bedlington Terrier from a rescue shelter. Most Bedlington Terriers from rescue shelters are free and the shelter just wishes you to make a donation. It is important to remember that rescue Bedlington Terriers may have health or behavioral issues due to their turbulent lives. Bedlington Terriers in rescue shelters are also hardly ever puppies and tend to be middle aged or older. However by getting your Bedlington Terrier from a rescue shelter allows you to give a Bedlington Terrier a better life than they would have had in the past. Most Bedlington Terriers that end up in shelters have been cruelly treated or abandoned and by adopting one you are giving the animal a chance to experience life in a loving home.

PUPPY CARE

When purchasing a Bedlington Terrier both first time owners and veteran owners normally opt for buying a puppy. Purchasing a puppy will allow you to establish a good and healthy relationship with your dog and will set the foundation for a long happy friendship. Another reason puppies are so popular is due to the fact that they are among some of the most adorable creatures on the planet! However caring for a new puppy is not the easiest thing. You will have to be prepared to make some huge lifestyles changes to accommodate your new puppy. The following section is a simple and concise guide to help you care for the new canine addition to your family.

Find a Good Vet

Before purchasing your puppy it is a good idea to research the vets in your local area. It is very important to find a vet that is local and highly qualified. The best way to find a good vet is by asking your friends, local dog walkers, local dog groomers, asking the breeder and researching online. Once you purchase your new puppy you should take it straight to your vet for a checkup. The checkup visit will make sure that your puppy is in good health and free from any serious birth defects or genetic health issues. Introducing your vet to your new Bedlington Terrier while it is young also allows for your puppy to become familiar with the vet – this can help avoid stress during later visits. By taking your puppy to the vet straight away, it also allows you to start a health care routine with your pet. It is important to set up a vaccination plan with your vet and also to discuss the best methods for control parasites (both internal and external).

Food

It is important to purchase food that is formulated specifically for puppies. A decent brand will have a statement from the Association of American Feed Control Officials (AAFCO), or your countries equivalent, on the packaging to ensure that the food you are purchasing is going to fulfil your puppy's nutritional requirements. Small and medium-sized breeds can start eating adult dog food when they are between 9 and 12 months of age. Larger breeds of dog should be fed on puppy kibbles until they reach 2 years of age. It is important to make sure that your puppy has cool, fresh and clean water available to them at all times.

Feeding Schedule

Puppies have a different feeding schedule to adult

dogs. Their feeding schedule changes as they get older. I recommend feeding your puppy on the following schedule:

- **6 – 12 weeks old:** 4 meals per day
- **3 – 6 months old:** 3 meals per day
- **6 – 12 months old:** 2 meals per day

Obedience Training

It is important to train your new puppy to be obedient. Obedience will allow your puppy to have a life full of positive interactions as well as forging a stronger bond between you and your pet. It is important to teach your puppy simple commands such as sit, stay, down and come. These commands will help to keep your dog safe and under control in any potentially dangerous situations. I recommend attending a local obedience training class. Obedience classes allow for you and your dog to learn the best methods for each process and command. Obedience classes also allow you, and your puppy, to interact with other people and dogs of all ages and from all backgrounds. It is important to remember that positive reinforcement has been proven to be a dramatically more effective process than punishment.

Bathroom Training

Housetraining is a priority if you want to keep your house clean! Before you start your housetraining it is important to locate a suitable location for your puppy to go to the bathroom. If your puppy has not had all of its vaccinations it is important to find a bathroom that is inaccessible to other animals. This will help to avoid your puppy getting any unnecessary viruses or diseases. There are three key tricks to keep in mind when you are attempting to housetrain your puppy: positive reinforcement, planning and patience. It is important positively praise your puppy when they go to the bathroom outside and not to punish them when inevitable accidents will happen. I recommend the following times to try and introduce your puppy to a bathroom routine:

- When you first wake up.
- When your puppy wakes up from any naps it might have.
- During and after physical exercise.
- After your puppy eats or drinks a lot of water.
- Immediately before bed time.

Be Social

The main way to avoid your puppy developing behavioral problems is to be social with it. At approximately 2 to 4 months old, most puppies will begin to accept other animals, people, places and experiences. It is important to start socializing your puppy with as many people and animals as possible. I recommend bringing your puppy to a dog park, to your friends or relatives houses, to dog friendly restaurants and to have other people accompany you while you walk your pet. By interacting with multiple different types of people and animals your puppy will learn to be more social and accepting.

Signs of Illness

It is important to watch your puppy closely to make sure that it is not exhibiting any signs of illness. Your puppy is at its most vulnerable stage of its development while also being at its most important stage of development. If you notice any of the following signs you should take your puppy to the vet immediately: lack of appetite, vomiting, lack of weight gain, lack of growth, diarrhea, pale gums, nasal discharge, inability to pass urine and stool, lethargy, swelling and difficulty breathing.

Spaying and Neutering

There are a lot of factors to considered when deciding if you should spay or neuter your puppy. Many owners refuse to spay or neuter their puppy due to the fact that they find it morally wrong and unnatural. However most owners do decide to have their pet neutered. Shelter euthanasia is the number one killer of dogs and companion animals throughout America. In Atlanta alone over 15 million dollars is spent annually on euthanizing unwanted dogs! The only way to avoid this is to have your pet spayed or neutered. Dogs face some discomfort if they are in heat or are unable to mate. Spaying and neutering creates no long term health problems for your pet. At the end of the day it is an important decision for you and your family to make. I advise talking it over with your vet and family/friends who have already been through the process.

DOG CARE

Once your puppy has grown up, or if you have purchased an adult Bedlington Terrier, you will need to change how you care for it.

Dog Food

There are so many different brands of dog food available: organic, all natural, hypo-allergenic, vegetarian and even vegan! Good dog food is vital to provide your pet with the nutrition it needs to reach its full potential both physically and mentally. Good nutrition helps your Bedlington Terrier fight disease, prevents obesity, minimizes your dog's chance of getting an illness and generally improves your Bedlington Terrier's overall health and happiness. It is important to remember that the advertising on dog food is aimed at humans – because I are the ones that pay for it! You should only feed your dog food that has been approved by the Association of American Feed Control (AAFCO) as it will ensure that the food is both safe and nutritious. You should look for brands of dog food that claim to have an 'AAFCO approved complete and balanced nutritional value' – it is illegal for a brand to claim that they have been approved by the AAFCO if they have not. Make sure the food you purchase contains protein, carbohydrates, fats, vitamins and minerals.

How much to Feed Your Bedlington Terrier

Unfortunately there is no exact method for figuring out exactly how much an individual Bedlington Terrier should eat. Determining the correct size meal depends on the type of dog food, how many times a day your dog eats, your dog's size and weight, your dog's metabolic rate, the amount of exercise they get and many other possible variants. Adult Bedlington Terriers are normally fed twice a day. I recommend looking at the feeding guide on the packaging of your dog's food. The feeding guide is normally recommends weights of food based upon your dog's weight. However this feeding guide is not necessarily accurate (your dog may struggle gaining weight or may gain weight at an increased rate). I recommend talking to your vet about how much you should be feeding your Bedlington Terrier. It also takes a bit of time to get used to your Bedlington Terrier and their eating habits.

Visits to the Vet

It is important to take your Bedlington Terrier to the vet on a regular basis. Regular visits to the vet can allow you to treat any issues your Bedlington Terrier has in the early stages to avoid them having a negative impact on your Bedlington Terrier's health. I recommend scheduling to see your vet at least twice a year – however more frequent visits are advantageous in identifying health problems! It is more important to prevent the onset of disease rather than treat them once they occur. With each visit to the vet you should make sure that you get your dog weighed. By getting your dog weighed on a regular basis you will know if you are feeding it the correct sized portions.

Exercise

Exercise is vitally important to keep your Bedlington Terrier happy, healthy and behaving correctly. Dogs, and puppies, have a lot of energy and may develop destructive behaviors if they are not allowed to burn off their energy. How much exercise a dog needs is dependent on its age, breed and health. Most Bedlington Terriers should be walked for at least 30 minutes a day – however I recommend walking your Bedlington Terrier for around 60 minutes a day to ensure it has gotten enough exercise. You will know when your Bedlington Terrier has had enough exercise when it has slowed its walking speed by a considerable amount. Good exercise uses both physical and mental muscles. I therefore recommend providing your Bedlington Terrier with multiple different sources of exercise such as: hiking, walking around your block (using different routines), taking your Bedlington Terrier to the park and taking your Bedlington Terrier swimming. If you provide your Bedlington Terrier with a lack of exercise they are likely to become obese. Obesity in Bedlington Terriers, like in humans, comes with a wide range of health issues. Obesity contributes to a dog developing diabetes, respiratory disease, heart disease and general ill health and tiredness. I recommend living by the following philosophy: a tired dog is a happy, healthy and good dog.

GROOMING

Grooming is an important aspect to caring for your Bedlington Terrier! Grooming includes caring for your Bedlington Terrier's coat, dental health, nails and over all cleanliness. Dogs enjoy getting messy so sometimes cleaning can be a chore! The following section will highlight all the aspects of grooming that you should consider.

Grooming Tools

- **Bristle Brush:** Bristle brushes are used for all breeds of dog. Bristle brushes help to keep your dog's coat shiny and free from dirt.
- **Clippers and Shedding Blade:** Most species of dog will need to have their coats trimmed in summer to keep them cool. I recommend using clippers for dogs with long coats and shedding blades for short hair dogs.
- **De-Matting Rake:** De-matting rakes have long wire prongs. These prongs are great for removing matts from long coats. It is important to use this tool gently to avoid causing your dog discomfort.
- **Rubber Brush:** Rubber brushes are great for removing dead hair. They create a massaging

effect which many dogs enjoy.

- **Slicker Brush:** Slicker brushes are used to remove tangles and dead hair. They have rows of bent wire pins. They should only be used on dogs with long or thick hair.
- **Nail Clippers:** Nail clippers should be scissor shaped to allow for best control. It is important to purchase sharp nail clippers and to always have a spare set (in case one set become blunt).
- **Nail File:** Nail files are used to file the end of your dog's toe nail after it has been clipped. It is important to purchase a high quality nail file as it will allow the filing process to be completed much quicker.

Grooming a Long Hair Dog

To groom a long haired Bedlington Terrier you should first go over their coat with a slicker brush. Make sure that you are brushing your pet gently to avoid causing any discomfort to your Bedlington Terrier as you remove tangles and dead hair. You should brush your dog's legs, tail, thighs, head and back. Once you have gone over the coat with a slicker brush you should then repeat the process with a bristle brush. Make sure to brush in the direction that the coat naturally settles in. The point of the bristle brush is to smooth out the detangled hair. Long haired dogs will need to be brushed on a daily basis. If you want to change the hairstyle of your Bedlington Terrier I recommend using clippers. When using clippers it is first important to visualize how you want your Bedlington Terrier's coat to look. You should use clippers on your dog's head, feet, legs, sides, underside and body. It is important to trim the fur away from your dog's eyes and muzzle – make sure to take extra care around your pet's eyes!

Grooming a Short Haired Dog

Short haired Bedlington Terriers should be brushed a minimum of once a week. Brushing your Bedlington Terrier's coat will stimulate natural oils in their skin and will also remove any dead hair. You should groom your short haired Bedlington Terrier by brushing all over its body with a slicker brush. Make sure to start at the head and work your way down. It is important to keep your Bedlington Terrier's coat taut as you brush to effectively remove dead hair. Once you have removed all of the Bedlington Terrier's dead hair you should brush the Bedlington Terrier's coat back into the position it naturally lies in. I recommend using a bristle brush or a rubber brush for this process. You can also comb your dog's coat. A short haired dog will not have excessive tangles in its coat and a fine toothed brush is a perfect way to make your dog's coat look perfect!

Bathing your Dog

Just like people, dogs need a good bathing schedule. Most Bedlington Terriers only require a bath once a month. However if your dog enjoys rolling around in mud and getting especially dirty, you may have to bathe it more often. It is not recommended to bathe your Bedlington Terrier more than once a week as it will lose the essential oils present on its skin. It is important to use a Bedlington Terrier friendly shampoo and conditioner when bathing your Bedlington Terrier as they are designed to not irritate your Bedlington Terrier's skin. If your dog has especially sensitive skin it is possible to purchase medicated shampoo to decrease the chance of irritating your dog. I recommend washing your dog in either your bath tub or shower, as it is the least likely to create a watery mess! It is considered best practice to provide your pet with a non-slip mat to keep them secure in the shower or bath tub. Before bathing your dog make sure to have your shampoo and a towel ready to hand. While bathing your pet you should keep one hand on your Bedlington Terrier at all times to make sure it does not leave the bath / shower. If your Bedlington Terrier is worried about the bathing process reward them with treats to encourage them to relax. You should aim to massage your Bedlington Terrier during the shampooing and toweling process to make the bathing experience more pleasurable and fun for them.

Brushing your Dogs Teeth

In America it is estimated that 80% of dogs have some form of dental disease by 3 years of age! Bedlington Terriers, like humans, need to have their teeth cleaned to remove bacteria and tartar build up. If you do not clean your Bedlington Terrier's teeth they are likely to develop Periodontal disease which affects the base of the tooth near the gum line. Bedlington Terriers can also suffer from dental disease such as gingivitis. It is recommend using a meat flavored toothpaste to reward your Bedlington Terrier when it lets you brush its teeth – these toothpastes have the added benefit of being nontoxic if swallowed! You can use a regular toothbrush or a finger brush for the cleaning process. Make sure that the brush has soft bristle to avoid damaging your Bedlington Terrier's teeth and gums. Aim to brush each individual tooth for around 5 seconds. It is considered best practice to brush your Bedlington Terrier's teeth on a daily basis. Daily cleaning is the best way to prevent dental problems and to keep your Bedlington Terrier's breath smelling dramatically better!

Ear Cleaning

Dogs have very long ear canals (around 5 to 10cm in length) that have a right angled bend in them. The bend means that foreign objects can easily get into your Bedlington Terrier's ear canal but are very hard to get out! If your Bedlington Terrier gets water in its ear, the water can pool at the bend and cause ear infections due to the warm, moist and dark environment of the ear. You should ask your vet how often you should clean your Bedlington Terrier's ears, but as a rule of thumb: no more than once a week and no less than once a month. To clean your Bedlington Terrier's ears you will need ear cleaner, cotton wool and treats to reward your dog during the potentially uncomfortable process. There are multiple different brands of ear cleaner available and it is important to choose a good quality product. I recommend asking you vet for their suggestion as most pet stores will stock different brands. Once you have the products to hand it is time to start the cleaning process. Gently hold the flap of your dog's ear upright and fill the ear canal with the ear cleaner. It is important to aim the ear cleaner directly downwards as you use it. Once the ear cleaner is in place, massage the skin around your dog's ear to mix the ear cleaner with the contents of your Bedlington Terrier's ear canal. Do this for around 20 seconds. Once the massaging time is up, stand up and move away from your dog. Your dog will shake its head vigorously to remove some of the ear cleaner. Once your dog has stopped shaking its head, grab the cotton wool and use it to wipe the folds at the opening of your Bedlington Terrier's ear canal until it looks clean. Make sure to reward your Bedlington Terrier before and after the ear cleaning process to relax it.

Nail Clipping

It is important to trim your Bedlington Terrier's toe nails every two weeks to keep them properly maintained. If you allow your pet's toe nails to grow too long it will cause your Bedlington Terrier discomfort as it walks – the long term consequence of walking on overly long toe nails is arthritis! It is important to use clippers that resemble scissors as they provide the most control while clipping your Bedlington Terrier's nails. It is also considered best practice to use small clippers as they again allow for better control. Make sure that your clippers are sharp before attempting to clip your pet's nails. Gently separate your Bedlington Terrier's fingers for clipping – never squeeze your Bedlington Terrier's toe as they will cause them to be in pain. It is considered best practice to have an assistant during the clipping process as they are able to secure your dog in place and distract it's attention. You should aim to make the clipping process and a positive experience so your dog feels at ease – use positive praise and treats to promote a positive atmosphere! It is IMPORTANT to note that all Bedlington Terriers have a vein that run through their fingers called a 'quick.' If you cut off too much of your dog's nail it is possible to cut into the 'quick' which will cause your Bedlington Terrier to bleed. Although not fatal it is still to be avoided as it will cause your pet unnecessary discomfort. If you do accidentally cut the 'quick' you should stop the bleeding by dabbing a little cornstarch onto the nail with a cotton swab. It is also possible to file your Bedlington Terrier's nail or have a vet cut your pet's nails for you (although this will have a fee). If you are worried about trimming your dog's nails I recommend taking your Bedlington Terrier to a vet once to have them demonstrate how to trim your pet's nails correctly.

TRAINING

It would seem that Bedlington Terriers enjoy being trained due to the fact that they both enjoy the human interaction of the training process and seem to enjoy 'pleasing' their owners. Training your Bedlington Terrier is a perfect way to strengthen the bond between you and your pet as well as being a cool thing to show to non-dog owners.

The Key Components of Training

The following bullet points are the five most important aspects of training any animal:

- Trust
- Positive reinforcement
- Repetition
- Patience
- Consistency

Pre-requisites for successful training

It is vital that your Bedlington Terriers are well socialized and accustomed to both your presence and being handled by you. It is not a good idea to try to train new Bedlington Terriers immediately after purchasing them as they will not trust you and may be frightened or stressed by the training process. Younger Bedlington Terriers, and puppies, are generally more adaptable to training and will therefore pick up new tricks at a faster rate. However younger Bedlington Terriers will also have a shorter attention span which can make the process of training them a long process. Older Bedlington Terriers will have a longer attention span but may be less willing to do physical based training.

Preparation

Before starting to train your Bedlington Terrier it is best to know how your Bedlington Terrier enjoys spending it's time and what food it loves so you can reward it appropriately. It is important to find one or two healthy treats to reward your Bedlington Terrier with to help them stay healthy and motivated during the training process. I recommend rewarding your Bedlington Terrier with the following treats: raw carrot, a liver treat or a small piece of chicken. The reason it is important to know your pet Bedlington Terrier's preferences is to allow you to work with your pet's natural inclinations and to praise and positively re-enforce the behavior you want.

Clicker Training

Clicker training is considered the easiest and most

effective way to train Bedlington Terriers. The concept behind the training is that the clicker tells your Bedlington Terrier when they have correctly performed a trick or action. Using a click also allows you to signal to your dog that they have done something correct from a long distance away. Clickers allow you to shape your dog's behavior, which means praising and rewarding closer and closer approximations to the behavior or trick you wish to teach. A click should always be paired with a treat. This allows your dog to create an association between 'clicks' and treats which will encourage your dog to obey clicks. You can purchase a specialized dog training clicker from any pet store or online. Before using the clicker in training, you should pair a click with a reward. Simply click then give your dog a treat. Then wait a few seconds and repeat the process. Repeat this around 10 to 15 times so your dog knows to associate clicks with treats before the training session has even begun.

Teaching Focus and Attention

The fundamental aspect of training a Bedlington Terrier is to teach the Bedlington Terrier to pay attention to you. You should say the dog's name and then reward them for their attention once they give it to you. Repeat this process several times to ensure that your dog will respond with the appropriate level of attention when you call its name. It is important to shape your Bedlington Terrier's behavior through positive reinforcement until you can get your dog to give you full focus – including eye contact.

General Training Tips

The most important training tip is to make sure that you always keep training session short. Short training session will reduce the chance of your dog becoming frustrated and will likewise enhance its concentration. I recommend keeping all training session between 10 and 15 minutes in length. Remember to always reward your Bedlington Terrier after clicking to reinforce the likelihood that they will obey clicks. If you are teaching a tricky command, I recommend giving your dog a 'jackpot' of treats when they do the desired trick. By giving your dog more treats than normal will signify that they have done the correct action. It is considered best practice to never end on a failure! If your Bedlington Terrier has not fully come to terms with a new trick, you should end the training session by rewarding your pet for completing a trick they already know. This will keep your Bedlington Terrier looking forward to training sessions.

Avoid Punishment

Dogs do not learn well by being punished. Punishment will normally make your Bedlington Terrier feel confused, stressed and scared – which are not good mental states to be in for learning! A dog that destroys a piece of furniture and looks guilty is responding to your anger rather than knowing what they did was wrong. If your dog is doing something destructive I recommend clapping your hands loudly, or calling its name, to get its attention. Once you have its attention you should lead its focus onto a more productive activity.

What if the training is not working?

It is important that you go into the training process with the intention of having fun and bonding with your pet – any tricks your pet learns will be an added bonus! It is very uncommon for a Bedlington Terrier to be untrainable. If the training is not working it is important to think about if you have a close relationship with the Bedlington Terrier you are trying to train and if your Bedlington Terrier is in the correct mind set to learn tricks. Bedlington Terriers can easily become bored of repeated training and may likewise be disinterested due to the time of day. Another reason for a dog's disinterest may be that you are offering them the wrong type of treat as a reward. It is important to remember that dogs, like humans, learn at different rates and some Bedlington Terriers will therefore take longer to train. If a Bedlington Terrier seems impossible to train it is probably advisable to stop trying to train it and just enjoy playing with it and caring for it.

TRAVELING WITH YOUR DOG FOR LOCAL TRIPS

Driving with a dog in your car can be problematic. Sometimes your dog will whine, bark, move around in a haphazard manner or even throw up. Driving can give some dogs anxiety which can lead to some unpleasant long drives! This section will outline 7 rules that will allow your pawed pet to feel more comfortable in the care – which will make both your, and your pets, traveling lives much more relaxing and enjoyable.

Patience and Planning

The first most important thing to remember when introducing your dog to your car is that patience is definitely required. You should let your dog explore your car well in advance of their first car journey. If you introduce your dog to the car on the day of its first journey – this is probably too late and may lead to your dog suffering from anxiety or being over whelmed by the whole experience. It is important to plan a series of 'exercises' to introduce your dog to your car. Firstly, you could allow it to spend some time exploring your car: the back seats, the boots, the front seats and all the cubby holes. Secondly you could take your dog on a short practice car ride: maybe around your block or just forward and backwards on your drive. This is important as it lets your dog become comfortable with the motion of the car. Some dogs will become nervous at the unfamiliar motion but with reassurance, treats and patience they will be able become more comfortable with the car. Another useful technique is to feed your dog on the backseat of your car for a few days. This builds up a positive association with the car which can be invaluable for dogs with an especially nervous temperament.

Mark the Territory with Scent

No matter how used to your car a dog will get, car rides will always be a source of excitement and adventure. This makes it highly important to allow your dog to mark their territory within your car. This could be done by allowing your dog to have a specific seat in the car, or boot, that they can identify as their space. This will allow them to become familiar with the space which will lead them to become more easily relaxed. One way to help your dog to mark its territory is to bring its favorite toys, blankets and cushions into the car. Adding your dog's favorite things, which will already be covered in their scent, is a great way to make your dog feel comfortable and relaxed in your car.

Security

It is important to focus on the security and safety of your four-legged friend during all car excursions. This may mean that you install a partition between the passenger area and the boot of your car to stop your dog being able to disrupt your focus while driving. Other common methods to secure your dog are: dog carriers and specialized doggy seatbelts. It is important to note that different countries, states and areas may have completely different rules and regulations concerning transporting dogs in your car. It is important to look up the traffic codes in your local area and anywhere you wish to travel. This will ensure your dog is safe and may also avoid you receiving any unpleasant traffic violation fines.

Pit Stops

While on a long drive everyone wants to have a break. For humans this might mean a snack and a coffee at a service station or a short break in a scenic area. When you are bringing your dog on the road with you, it is important to plan ahead. Check the route for pit stop destinations that will allow your dog to stretch their legs, go to the toilet, eat, drink and burn off some steam. Keeping a canine cooped up in a small space for a long period of time heightens the chance of your pet misbehaving or having a toilet accident. Most routes will have scenic walks, dog friendly establishments and rest areas that are suited for taking a quick break with your dog.

Exiting the Vehicle

It is important to **ALWAYS** exit your vehicle before you let your dog exit. If you let your dog exit the car before you it could lead to traffic accidents, your dog running away or your dog running into the road. When exiting the vehicle, it is best practice to:

1. Check that your dog is secure
2. Ext the vehicle
3. Walk around to the exit closet to your dog (car door, window or trunk)
4. Make eye contact with your dog and give a clear command to stay
5. Open the exit
6. Give a command for your dog to exit
7. Attach a leash or harness if necessary

Giving clear commands to your dog allows for you to remain in control of the situation. This can also help nervous or excitable dogs to retain focus.

Food and Water

It is important to limit your dog's food and water intake before a journey. If your pet has consumed to much food, they might throw up. If your pet has drank too much water, they may have to use the bathroom well in advance of your first pit stop. Both of these scenarios can lead to your dog feeling unwell, and it may also lead you to feeling unwell due to any unpleasant smells. It is important to limit the amount of snacking and drinking your dog can do in the car, but it is also important to provide sustenance for your dog during long trips. Finding the correct balance can take some time, as the balance is different for each dog. The best way to make sure a dog is unlikely to become travel sick during a journey is to allow them to build their confidence and comfortableness inside a moving vehicle on shorter practice journeys.

Overheating

Dogs are prone to overheating while inside cars for prolonged periods of time. If you have to make a long journey with your dog, it might be a good idea to make a sheltered space. This could be done by laying a blanket over a section of your car or boot. A shadowy space can definitely help your dog keep cool. Another way to minimize discomfort for your dog on hot days is to provide them with cool water, ice cubes or a wet flannel you can put on their head. If you are planning on exiting your car and leaving your dog inside it is HIGHLY important to limit how long your dog is left inside the car. Dog can overheat very quickly and a car in direct sunlight can become unbearably hot for a dog. I suggest never leaving your dog in a locked car. Opening the car window slightly is not enough to keep your pet cool. Your dog's health and safety is of vital importance, don't take the chance and take your dog with you when you exit the car.

TRAVELING WITH YOUR DOG INTERNATIONALLY

Most people purchase a dog when they have decided to settle down and start a family. Most people believe that it is difficult to travel internationally with a dog – this leads a lot of people to not want a dog during their young wanderlust years. What if I was to tell you that there are ways for a dog lover to travel internationally with their furry friend? Dogs are considered by many to be a human's best friend, why would you want to leave your best friend at home while you explore the world? Bring your dog with you!

Where to travel with your dog

When you are planning your next adventure, it is important to consider the climate, time of year and weather forecast. For example, you would not want to take a long-haired dog to Africa during the heart of summer, similarly you would not want to take a breed like a Chihuahua to a cold climate during the winter months. Dogs generally are highly adaptive creatures, but it is not worthwhile acclimatizing your pet to dramatically different climates for the purpose of a short trip.

If you are planning on taking your dog to a very

different climate you can always take accessories to make the change in temperature easier to adapt to. For example, you can bring warm jumpers, coats and snow boots for you dog if you are going to a cold climate. If you are taking your dog to a hot climate you might consider bring it a pair of shoes (the hot ground can become uncomfortable for unprepared paws) or a cooling jacket. Cooling jacket can be filled with water and work similar to an ice pack. A cheap cooling jacket is the 'Go Fresh Pet Ice Colling Dog Vest' made by 'Pets at Home' and costs a reasonable $15.

When planning a trip with your pet it is important to take into account your pet's personality. Some dogs, like humans, do not like to be away from their homely comforts. If you are planning on traveling with your pet, it is advisable to take your dog with you everywhere during its puppyhood as a method of introducing it to the traveling lifestyle.

Regulations

Before deciding on when and where to travel, it is first a good idea to check the regulations of the airlines, boarder control and transportation services you will encounter during your travel. Each country will have different regulations surrounding importing dogs. Some countries will have strict importation regulations surrounding pets, while others are more lenient.

If you are traveling from a rabies free country around mainland Europe most countries only require your pet to be microchipped and have had a rabies vaccination. However, countries such as the United Kingdom, Norway, Finland and Malta need your dog to have had an additional tapeworm treatment. If you are traveling from a country that is not rabies free you will need proof (proof last for a year) that your dog has had a rabies antibody blood test.

Some countries, such as Australia, have quarantine regulations which means your dog will have to be test on arrival by a government lab. This normally takes a minimum of ten days! For countries who have quarantine laws you will also need an important permit, veterinary certificates and recent rabies blood tests.

The most reliable source for checking the importation regulations is: www.pettravel.com. This website lists all the regulations for all the countries of the world and is an invaluable source for anyone looking to travel with their dog.

Method of Travel

There are a lot of different methods to travel with your dog; by car, by plane, by boat, by coach and by train to name but a few. Each method of travel will raise its own problems and challenges.

If you are planning on taking your pet on a flight it is important to note that there are three main methods: taking your dog with you in the cabin of the plane, checking your dog as baggage or booking your dog to be taken on a separate cargo flight. Most airlines will have regulation that allow dogs of up to 46cm length, 28cm width and 24cm height with a maximum weight of 8kg. Most airlines will not allow you to have your dog outside of a container if it is traveling on the cabin. The reason for this is that airlines are worried dogs may run up and down the aisle during dinner time which may disturb other customers.

If a dog is too big for the cabin it will have to be checked as baggage. The baggage hold is temperature and pressure regulated so your pet will be fine once in the air. The only concern when checking your pet into the baggage hold is the fact that your pet will be exposed to the elements during loading and unloading. If you are leaving from, or arriving at, an especially cold airport this could cause your dog health problems.

Airports with high heat and humidity are also a concern – for example the Emirates airline will not allow dogs to be transported in baggage bet5ween 1st May and 30th September as the heat and humidity are dangerously high. When booking a flight with a pet please priorities short and direct flights if possible!

If you cannot fly with your pet, you can book your pet a flight with a cargo service. There are plenty of cargo services that specialize in the transportation of animals. The only downside of booking a cargo flight for your dog is that you and your dog may not arrive at the destination at the same time, or even day. Some cargo flights will also land at non-commercial airports – which can mean you have to travel to pick up your pet once at your destination.

Most commercial boat lines have kennels on board. Most boat lines have a regulation that once onboard all dogs must stay in their kennels. This is to prevent the potential for accidental an overboard. It is important to note that on long journeys this may not be the best option as boat line kennels are not always the most comfortable and spacious.

Most trainlines worldwide will allow dogs to be transported upon them. Some trainline companies have regulation that dogs have to be on a leash or in a dog crate for the entirety of the journey. Some countries, such as Vietnam, do not allow dogs on trains,

Traveling by car is by far the best option! It allows you to control the pace of your journey and to allow your four-legged friend to have as many pit stops, food breaks and exercise breaks. Car journeys are also least likely to cause your dog stress as they are likely to be a normal occurrence.

Traveling Equipment

Here is a useful list of equipment you can purchase to make traveling with your dog easier:

- A waist harness: A waist harness will allow you to keep your hands free while keeping your dog in control and next to you. Waist harnesses are especially useful for anyone hiking as it allows you to fully access your map. Waist harnesses are also very useful when you need two hands to transport your luggage to the correct location.
- IATA (International Air Transportation Association) pet crate: An IATA pet crate will help minimize any problem you may have checking your dog into the baggage compartment of a plane or keeping it in the cabin with you. Most airlines will accept crates with air holes on all sides, made of a sturdy plastic, have a wire door and have a secure locking

system. It is best practice to purchase a IATA crate though as it will definitely lead to less potential hassle.

- Pet Passport: Some countries, including all countries within Europe, require your pet to have their own passport. Pet passports state when you pet has last received vaccination for diseases – such as rabies. Most vets will issue pet passports but if they do not, I would recommend asking the vet to tell you where the closest location to get a pet passport is. Pet passports come with a lot of space for you to update the medical history of your pet.

Arrival

Having a fixed plan for your arrival can definitely help to minimize stress, for yourself and your dog. Have you booked accommodation that allows for pets? Have you plotted a route that will allow you easy access to food and water for your dog? Have you checked, and abided by, all local laws concerning dogs? As previously mentioned, flying your pet on a pet specific cargo flight is a highly popular choice. If this is the case – have you planned to get to where the cargo flight is landing? Have you made accommodations for your dog to be looked after if you cannot get to them straight away? Please don't ruin your trip through lack of preparation!

BREEDING

We previously did not include a section on how to breed dogs. The main reason for this is that this series of books is designed for first time dog owners and beginners. Breeding is a complicated and potentially risky business. One of the main reasons I decided to not include a breeding section is that breeding laws are widely different from country to country. Before beginning to breed any animal, you should check the local laws, regulations and best practices. However due to popular demand the following section will give a **BREIF** overview on the breeding process. This guide should not be used as your only resource if you plan to become a breeder!

IMPORTANT NOTE: IF YOU ARE SERIOUS ABOUT BECOMING A DOG BREEDER, I **URGE** YOU TO CONTACT YOUR LOCAL KEENLE CLUB AND ASK FOR ADVICE, OR SOMEONE THEY CAN PUT YOU IN TOUCH WITH. BREEDING DOGS CAN LEAD TO A PLETHORA OF PROBLEMS. HEIR ON THE SIDE OF SAFTEY AND PLEASE ASK YOUR LOCAL KENNEL CLUB FOR HANDS ON ADVICE AND SUPPORT.

Before Breeding Begins

Dog breeding has been a big part of human history – dogs have been donned 'man's best friend' for a reason. Before breeding a litter, it is important to first gain as much information as you can. You should spend time studying the 'breed standard,' which will give you an outline on what a 'perfect' specimen of that breed will look and behave like. The AKC is has an amazing set of resources about breeding such as: illustrated guides, video guides and many written guides. Before breeding you must prepare yourself for the trails, successes, unexpected surprises and potential heart breaks that come hand in hand with the breeding process.

Before breeding it is important to assess the quality of your dog. Every loving dog owner thinks that their dog is the best, most loveable and cutest dog in the world. This idea does not always help in the breeding process. If you plan on breeding your current dogs it would be a good idea to assess their 'quality' before breeding them. This can be done by entering your dog into a dog show, this will allow you to compare your dog to other dogs in their breed. It is important to remember that breeding is about 'improving' the quality, temperament and physical health of your litter.

Before breeding it is important to note that raising

a litter of puppies is a hard and long full-time job! While it is very easy to romanticize the idea of caring for a group of puppies, the reality can be very tiring, time consuming, messy and at time over whelming. Some puppies can become semi uncontrollable during the weaning phase. The extra feeding, grooming, training, trips to the vet and vet bills can add up in time and money. Another important aspect to breeding is making sure that your puppies go to good homes. This can mean researching, background checking and screening potential owners. Breeding is a big commitment!

Choosing a mating pair

The first thing to consider when you are starting the breeding process is; do you want to breed purebred dogs or mixed dogs? If want to make mixed dogs the coupling process can be easier. If you want to make purebred dogs it is important to choose a Dam (bitch) and a Sire (male dog) that have been registered to a Kennel Club. If both the Sire and Dam are registered to a Kennel Club the litter can be automatically registered.

When you are selecting a breeding partner for your dog the most important thing to remember is to pick a coupling that compliments each other. Choose a partner that comes from a strong blood lines, have no health problems, has a good temperament and matches the type of coat you want your litter to have. For example, if your dog has a 'bad' coat it may be worth coupling them with a dog that comes from a long line of dogs with 'good' coats. While this idea may seem simple in principle it can actually be very difficult – when looking at a dog it is very difficult to actually comprehend their strengths and weaknesses in a cohesive way. It is best practice to write down the strengths of a dog and then write down its weaknesses. This gives you a resource to go home and think over your choice. When it comes to breeding being particular is not a bad thing!

The most important factors to considers are health and temperament.

Health issues are hereditary in dogs. You should ask the owner of any potential mates to provide a medical history for their dog and their dog's ancestor (if possible). As a breeder one of your main goals should be to breed dogs that do not suffer from any of the main illnesses, genetic deformities and diseases that affect dogs (there will be an outline of the most common diseases, illnesses and genetic problems that affect dogs in a later section). Temperament is mostly a hereditary trait. This can allow you track the temperaments of your dog and your dog's potential mates. It is not worth breeding your dog with a 'perfect' breed standard dog if it has a nasty, misbehaving or mean temperament.

If you do not own the dog you are choosing as your dog's mating partner, you will have to create and finalize a stud contract. A stud contract should include fees, obligations and who has ownership of the litter of puppies. Stud contracts may include payment of cash, a 'pick of the litter' or a designated number of puppies from the litter (this can be done as a lottery or by the choice of the litter's owner). A stud contract should be signed by both parties and both parties should receive a copy of the finalized contract.

Importance of Genetics

As previously mentioned, – your dog's health and temperament will be determined by the genetics passed down to them by their parents and grandparents. It is important to note that, like in humans, hereditary problems are capable of skipping on or two generations. Do not judge the 'quality' of a dog based on its temperament and aesthetic alone. Genetics are not obvious by looking at a dog, interacting with a dog or listening to a dog – this is why it is important to examine the pedigree of your potential mating couple. It is important to become knowledgeable about the genetic problems that tend to affect your breed. The following is a quick guide on how to spot potential problems:

- Dominant Genetics – some diseases, illnesses and genetic disorders follow a dominant genetic pattern. A dominant genetic is one that will always be passed on and only need one mutant gene. If only one of the parents carried a dominant gene, then the disorder will appear in all subsequent generations.
- Recessive Genes – some disorders can only appear in dogs that have one mutant gene from their mother and one mutant gene from their father. Dogs who suffer from these genetics are called homozygous. Dogs who only have one mutant gene are called heterozygous. Both homozygous and heterozygous dogs will pass their mutant genetics on to their offspring. Recessive mutant gene can pass through generations dormant until a mating couple, who both carry the gene, are paired together. It is **VERY** important to research the medical history of your breeding couple's ancestry.
- Polygenic Disorders – Polygenic disorders are a result of the action of multiple 'bad' genes. Polygenic disorders are very difficult to track as it is hard to determine what concoction of genes is creating the disorder. Polygenic disorders can sometimes appear as either a Dominant gene or a Recessive gene which makes them especially hard to identify.

Pre-Breeding Health Checks

The vital steps in producing a good 'quality' litter of puppies happens well in advance of the actually mating process. It is important to ensure that the mating pair have had recent medical checks. Mating pairs need to have had multiple screenings for genetic problems, have had regular visits to the vets, have had a nutritious diet and received enough exercise. Bitches should not be overweight before the mating begins. It is a good idea to thoroughly exercise both dogs until they are toned and well-muscled. It is important to note that a Bitch who is in a good mental state will produce a better litter and will also provide better care to their young.

It is a good idea to have both of the mating pair test for brucellosis. Brucellosis is an infectious form of bacteria that can lead to sterility and spontaneous abortions. Both of the breeding pair should also be completely up to date on their vaccinations and good through a pre-breeding physical performed by a vet.

The age in which your dog becomes sexually active is dependent on the purity of the breed, the dog's ancestral history and their genetics. Male dogs will normally become fertile at around 6 months of age, hit their full sexual maturity at around 12-15 months and are capable of breeding well into their old age. Female dogs normally go into 'heat' (also known as Estrus) at around 6 months – although it can occur later. Female dogs will enter heat at intervals of approximately 6 months until their old age. It is important to note that most Kennel Clubs will not allow a litter to be registered if their mother is under 8 months of age. It is considered best practice to not breed a bitch during her first heat. This is due to the fact that most breeders believe it to be uncompassionate to put a young animal through the physical and mental stress associated with lactation, pregnancy and giving birth. It is also considered best practice to not breed a female dog on consecutive heats as their bodies need time to recuperate after pregnancy.

How To Identify If Your Female Dog Is Fertile

The following section will give a guideline on how to know whether or not your bitch is ready for breeding. There are four main stages in a female dog's cycle: Proestrus, Estrus, Diestrus, Anestrus.

- Proestrus: – Proestrus is the phase that begins before a female goes into heat. Proestrus can be identified by bloody vaginal discharges and your dog having a swollen vulva. This phase last for around 9 days and will involve your female dog attract potential mates. No breeding will take place during this period.

- Estrus: - Estrus lasts for around 9 days. This is when the mating process will take place. The female will accept being fertilized by the male during this period. Ovulation normally occurs during the first 48 hours of Estrus. Some females will allow multiple mating session – others will not. It is considered best practice to try and initiate a mating session between the 48-hour and 72-hour mark.
- Diestrus: - Diestrus lasts for around 2 to 3 months. During this period the female's reproductive tract is under the control of their progesterone hormone. This will happen whether or not the female dog has become pregnant.
- Anestrus: - During Anestrus the female dog will have no interest in sexual contact. This period lasts for between 3 and 4 months.

Natural Breeding

When it comes to natural breeding, most breeders will introduce the mating pair around the 10th or 13th day after the onset of proestrus. If the mating process is successful, most breeders will encourage the pair to mate every other day for two to three attempts.

It is important to note that proestrus is not visible in a lot of female dogs. It is considered best practice to have a vet examine your dog's hormones in advance of the mating process.

Female dogs are generally less inhibited by their environment during the mating process. This makes it a common practice for the female dog to be taken to the male dog for the breeding. Male dogs are much more territorial and therefore feel more comfortable mating in environments they feel confident in. Breeding involving young studs and experienced bitches tend to go most smoothly. It is not uncommon for a handler to assist in guiding young dogs during the process. It is a good idea to determine who will assist in the breeding during the finalization of the stud contract.

During the mating process, the male will mount the female from the rear. Penetration and ejaculation can be incredibly quick or a slow process – it depends on the confidence, experience and compatibility of the mating pair. After ejaculation occurs the stud and bitch will not separate for around 15 to 30 minutes. This is known as a 'tie.' It is **HIGHLY** important to not attempt to separate the mating pair during a 'tie.' A 'tie' occurs because the stud's penial gland engorges effectively 'trapping' the pair together. This is a biological method employed across the animal kingdom and is implemented to heighten the chance of a successful fertilization. Attempting to separate the mating pair during a 'tie' can lead to the mating failing or the genitals of both dogs being injured. After the pair is ready – they will separate naturally.

Artificial Insemination

Artificial Insemination is implemented when natural breeding is impractical. Most Kennel Clubs will accept and register litters who have been created through artificial insemination. However, they will only accept litters produced with fresh sperm, extended sperm or frozen sperm. Artificial insemination is a simple process. It involves transferring the sperm into the female's vagina, near the cervix. If you are considering using artificial insemination, please seek the assistance of your vet as they are trained, and qualified, in the procedure.

Nutrition for a Pregnant Dog

A healthy bitch should continue her diet. Her pregnant caloric intake should match what her regular caloric intake is. **HOWEVER**, as her body weight increases so must her caloric intake – this occurs around 5 weeks before whelping. You should gradually increase your dog's caloric intake until it is about 135-150% of what it normally is. Some dogs will not want one or two large meals – it is therefore considered best practice to start offering your dog smaller, but more frequent, meals.

Whelping and the Whelping Box

Whelping is the term given to the act of a female dog giving birth. Most whelping happens inside the whelping box – a designated area for the birthing to happen. It is important to create the whelping box well in advance of your dog's due date. This will give her time to become accustomed and used to the whelping area, which helps to minimize stress during the birthing. If a whelping boxing is accepted and known, your dog might choose her own whelping area. This could be your closet, behind the couch or in the bath – which can lead to a lot of mess and a lot of discomfort.

A perfect whelping box would have the following traits: dry, warm, quiet, draft-free and secluded. A good whelping box will also have low sides to allow ease of access during the pregnancy. It is considered best practice to have a small shelf on the side of the whelping box. This shelf will allow puppies to move out of the way of their still birthing mother. This allows the puppies to stay safe and also not distract their mother. A shelf is less necessary if you are watching the birthing and are actively moving the puppies to a nearby safe location. Most breeders line the whelping box with newspaper as it can easily be changed when soiled. After the whelping, the flooring is normally changed to a clean towel or a bath mat.

A List Of Suggest Whelping Equipment

Below is a list of all the supplies you will need during a whelping. This list is not the be all and end all of whelping equipment. Don't be afraid to make some alterations or additions to this list.

- Newspaper: - Newspaper can be used as an initial bedding for the mother and puppies. This can be used to line before, during and after the whelping.
- Bath Mats: - Bath mats can be used after the whelping is completed to give the puppies a better surface to stand on. If you are going to use a bath mat, make sure it is a non-slip bath mat to avoid unnecessary falls.
- Clean Towels: - Clean towels can be used to line the whelping box before, during and after the whelping. Clean towels can also be used to clean puppies after they have been birthed.

- Thermostat: - A thermostat can be used to check the temperature of your dog before she beings the whelping. A overly high or low temperature can be a signal of complications.
- Dental Floss: - Dental floss can be used to sever the puppy's umbilical cords. If you are using dental floss please make sure it isn't waxed, scented or flavored.
- Shelf: - As previously mentioned a shelf in the whelping box can help to protect puppies after birth.
- Heating Pad: - A Heating pad can be extremely useful for keeping puppies warm after the birthing.
- Scissors: - Scissors can be used to cut the puppy's umbilical cord and placenta. Make sure to use stainless steel scissors to minimize the chance of infection. Please use a new pair of scissors or a pair that has been sterilized (in boiling water).
- Iodine: - Iodine is useful to clean the puppy's abdominal region after their umbilical cord has been cut.

Signs Labor Is Approaching

The first sign that labor is approaching is that your dog will start building a an area to give birth. Hopefully this area is the designated whelping box. If your dog starts preparing an area that is not the whelping box you can try to encourage them to shift their 'nest' using treats and praise. If not you might have to make accommodation for your dog's chosen location.

Around 24 hours before the whelping commences, your dog's temperature will drop by 2-4 degrees. After the temperature drops, your dog's cervix will begin to dilate and the birth canal will open. During this period your dog may appear stressed, start panting and move around restlessly. This is perfectly normal and is nothing to worry about. Soon after this your dog will start straining and will start to give birth.

It is **VERY** important to keep your vet's number and the number of the local emergency clinic at hand during this process. Please contact your vet or the emergency clinic if any of the following things happen:

- Your dog is indicating they are in extreme pain
- Strong contractions are occurring, but birthing is not happening

- More than 2 hours passes between the birthing of puppies
- Your dog passes our or collapses
- Your dog passes a bloody or dark green fluid before the birth of the first puppy. (It is important to note that this is nothing to concern yourself with if the blood/green fluid is expelled after/during the birth of the first puppy)
- No signs of contractions, labor or preparation for labor occurs after 64 days of your dog's last mating session.
- One or more of the puppies are still born.

Aftercare

It is not uncommon for a female dog to not want to eat or drink much for 1 or 2 days after whelping. After this 2 day 'fast' they will need a high amount of nutrients and calories. If you have been feeding your dog a healthy diet and proper food, they will not need supplementation. If your dog goes for a long period without having proper nutrition, they may develop eclampsia. Eclampsia can be spotted by a dog whimpering excessively, a dog staggering or spasming, nervousness and unsteadiness. Eclampsia is an easily treatable condition but can be fatal if untreated. After whelping your female dog should return to the weight she was before breeding. For two or three weeks you will need to double or triple your dog's food intake. It is considered best practice to split your dog's feeding into 3 or 4 meals a day to avoid stress on their abdominal region.

There is a possibility that your bitch will suffer from a condition known as 'Canine Mastitis.' This condition will make her breasts a combination of firm to the touch (almost hard), red, hot, swollen and/or painful. If you think your bitch is suffering from this condition, contact a vet immediately! Canine Mastitis can happen for a few reasons: scratches from a puppy's claws or teeth, an infection or the puppies being weaned too early. A dog suffering from this condition may stop eating, stop allowing her puppies to feed or may generally just become agitated. While this condition is not necessarily fatal it can severely affect the calorie intake of the mother and puppies – which in turn can become fatal.

Caring For New Born Puppies

Puppies are relatively easy to look after. They require warmth, such as a heating pad, until they are able to thermoregulate their body temperature. If your puppies are overly cold, it can lead to stress and an increased chance of infection and illness. If your puppies are overly hot, it can lead to death. When setting up a pen for your puppies it is considered best practice to have a heating pad on one side of the pen and a cooler space on the other side. This will allow puppies to easily regulate their temperature. Puppies need an atmospheric temperature of around 90 degrees for the first 5 days of their lives. After the first week, this temperature can be steadily lowered until it reaches a temperature of 75 degrees at the end of the fourth week of life.

After whelping your bitch will be producing highly nutritious and high calorie milk. This milk is known as 'colostrum.' Your new puppies will need to consume colostrum as quickly as possible, at least within the first 24 hours of their life. Colostrum contains immunoglobulins which help to protect the new born puppies from infections that the mother is immune to.

Some puppies will be ignored, or 'orphaned,' by their mother and will have a hard time feeding. These puppies may have to be fed by hand. It is important to remember that cow's milk, a non-dairy substitute or any other milk is not going to contain the nutrients, immunoglobulins and calories of a mother's colostrum milk. You may have to double the amount an 'orphaned' puppy consumes to make up for the lack of calories and nutrients. It is important to note that puppies grow and gain weight very quickly. You will have to adjust the amount you hand feed a puppy each day. You should gradually increase the puppy's intake as they will be receiving twice as much fluid as their peers. Before feeding you should warm the formula to boy temperature to simulate the mother's breast.

Note: Never produce more milk than is necessary and do not store it for more than one use. Milk is a great medium for bacteria growth! You do not want to feed your puppy something that could lead them to get ill.

Weaning

There are many different ideas and schools of thought concerning when and how to wean puppies. You should discuss a weaning regiment with your vet to make sure that they understand how the dogs are feeding – this can help the vet deal with any complications if they arise. Most puppies will start the weaning process at around 2 to 5 weeks of age. Some breeders create 'gruel' for their puppies. This 'gruel' is a mixture of milk formula, ground dog food and water. Other breeders will offer their puppies a bowl full of warm milk. Weaning can take experimentation and experience. I highly suggest consulting your local Kennel Club, local breeders and your vet for advice.

To avoid an upset stomach, you should introduce the new feeding regiment slowly. Make sure to monitor your puppies for the first few weeks of the weaning process to make sure they are not throwing the food up!

ILLNESSESS

There are multiple factors that play a huge part on your Bedlington Terrier's health: your dog's genetics, the quality of veterinary care they receive, what they eat and how safe the environment they live in is. The following section aims to help you recognize the most common and major threats to your dog's health to allow you to treat and prevent them. Your Bedlington Terrier's health is vitally important to giving your Bedlington Terrier a chance at a long, happy and healthy life.

Hip Dysplasia

Hip dysplasia is a heritable condition that prevents the thighbone from fitting snugly into the hip joint. Hip dysplasia is common among Bedlington Terrier but does not affect them all. It normally has symptoms of pain and lameness. However, hip dysplasia does not always cause your Bedlington Terrier discomfort but it may develop into arthritis as your Bedlington Terrier ages. Hip dysplasia is incurable and Bedlington Terriers who have it should not be bred. When purchasing a puppy from a breeder you should ask for proof that neither of your puppy's parents have hip dysplasia.

Parasites

Dogs enjoy spending a lot of time outside where they lick and sniff everything, roll around in dirt and puddles and run through long grass. While they find these activities enjoyable they also lead to parasite infestations.

- **Fleas and Ticks:** Fleas and ticks are the most common parasites. Fleas breed incredibly quickly and a couple can turn into an infestation surprisingly quickly. Ticks can cause some very dangerous disease – such as Lyme Disease and Ehrlichoisis. You dog will repeatedly itch itself, either with its paw or against furniture, if it has a tick or flea infestation.
- **Skin Mites:** Skin mites are dramatically smaller than fleas and ticks. Skin mites live on, or burrow into, your Bedlington Terrier's skin and can cause sever discomfort and diseases such as Mange. The main symptoms of skin mites are itching, skin irritation, inflammation and hair loss.
- **Heartworms:** Heartworms are parasites that migrate through your Bedlington Terrier's internal system to their hearts and other major organs. Due to the locations they

infest, they are extremely dangerous and usually deadly! The most effective way to prevent heartworms is to use a monthly heartworm preventive – medication that can purchased from your vet. There are no symptoms for heartworms other than your Bedlington Terrier becoming very ill.

- **Intestinal Worms:** Intestinal worms are very common among puppies. If your dog has recently had a tick or fleas there is a good chance that they now have an intestinal tapeworm. If your Bedlington Terrier eats other Bedlington Terrier's feces there is also a high chance that they will have an intestinal worm of some sort. The most common way to know if your Bedlington Terrier has worms is to physically see the worms in your Bedlington Terrier's waste. The best method to keep your Bedlington Terrier worm-free is to have a vet perform a fecal test at least once a year.
- **Single Cell Parasites:** Single cell parasites live in your dog's digestive tract. They can cause both Giardia and Coccidiosis if left untreated. If you are giving your dog heartworm preventative medication you normally do not need to worry about single cell parasites as

the medication should kill them as well.

Cherry Eye

Cherry eye is a problem that more commonly affects certain breeds but can affect any dog. The main symptom of cherry eye is a large red swelling appearing at the inner corner of one your dog's eye. Cherry eye is caused by the prolapsing of a tear gland attached to your dog's third eyelid. The prolapsed gland swells forward and creates the red bulge. Cherry eye is not a vision threating illness but does cause your Bedlington Terrier a lot of discomfort. There are a lot of websites and guides for curing cherry eye at home but I recommend taking your Bedlington Terrier to the vet so it receives the best quality medical care from a trained professional. There are two surgical options, performed under general anesthetic, to treat cherry eye. The first is to remove the damaged tear gland completely. The second it to surgically manipulate the gland back into its correct position. I advise that you consult with your vet as to what the best course of action is for your Bedlington Terrier's specific case.

Incontinence

Incontinence can affect your Bedlington Terrier at any age. If your Bedlington Terrier has previously been housetrained, it is important to remember that a loss of bladder, or bowel, control is a physical problem not a behavioral one. Incontinence is most commonly found in older Bedlington Terriers, especially females. Incontinence is normally caused by the following reasons: a urinary tract infection, old age, stress and anxiety, neurological problems (such as seizures), recent spaying surgery, diseases and other health problems. If your dog is suffering from incontinence it is recommend to bring it straight to the vet. The vet will be able to diagnose what is causing the problems and will be able to provide a suitable solution.

Parvovirus

Canine parvovirus is the both highly contagious and most deadly viral disease that affects dogs and puppies. Puppies have an increased chance of catching this illness. Most un-vaccinated dogs who catch parvovirus will die. However, parvovirus is not a fatal illness is identified in its early stages. The best method to prevent parvovirus is to give your puppy, and Bedlington Terrier, a full course of medical shots to provide it with strong protection and immunity from the virus. It is also vital to keep your puppy away from other Bedlington Terriers and animals before they have been fully vaccinated! The symptoms for parvovirus are: vomiting, lethargy, a fever and diarrhea. These symptoms are very common for a lot of other less serious illnesses but you should still take your pet to the vet if you notice any as you do not want to risk your dog having untreated parvovirus.

Dental Problems

Most dental problems in dogs are cause by periodontal disease. Periodontal disease can affect more than just your Bedlington Terrier's mouth and gums! If your Bedlington Terrier has rotten teeth and highly damaged gums they are more likely to catch other illnesses. More dental hygiene can cause your Bedlington Terrier to commonly get inflammations throughout their body. The best way to provide your dog with top quality dental care is to provide it with a chew toy. Chew toys allow your dog to strengthen their teeth and jaw as well as removing tartar! There are also multiple different types of doggy dental treats available which are designed to clean your dog's teeth and freshen their breath – Win Win! It is also considered best practice to clean your Bedlington Terrier's teeth, either by taking your pet to a professional dental cleaning service, a veterinary clinic or by brush your Bedlington Terrier's teeth yourself using a toothbrush. You should strive to make dental care a core part of your dog's grooming routine. The key signs for a dental disease are: excessive drooling, loss of appetite, difficulty eating, broken teeth, loose teeth, inflamed gums, tartar buildup and very pale gums. If you notice any of the above symptoms I recommend taking your dog to the vets.

Ear Problems

The majority of ear problems are relatively easy to treat once they are diagnosed. Ear problems can either be chronic (reoccurring) or acute (one off). Ear infections are one of the most common type of ear problem found in Bedlington Terriers. Ear infections normally occur in the external ear canal and have symptoms of ear redness, scabs and discharge around your dog's ear canal. This type of ear infection is called 'Otitis' and is caused by either a bacterial infection, a yeast or fungal infection, allergies or over exposure to water (such as swimming and bathing). The second most common type of ear problem is an infestation of ear mites. If your dog has ear mites there will be symptoms of black discharge around the ear canal, redness and inflammation of the ear canal, scabbing and a very strong odor. It is best practice to take your dog to the vet if they have any of the above symptoms as the vet will be able to identify the cause of the problem and be able to provide your dog with the best type of medical care. It is considered best practice to not clean your dog's ears before taking them to the vet – your vet will need to see the symptoms of your dog's ear problem. Most ear problems can be corrected through a treatment of oral medication or ear drops.

DANGEROUS FOODS

When owning any pet it is important to know what you should and should not be feeding it. Dogs are no exception to this! There are multiple different foods that can cause sever health problems in Bedlington Terriers – some can even be fatal! Foods that are commonly eaten by humans (both healthy foods and indulgent foods) can be incredibly toxic to Bedlington Terriers. It is important to educate your family and guests on what a Bedlington Terrier can and can't eat to avoid someone feeding it something that could damage its health. The following section will outline foods that you should NEVER give to your dog:

Avocado

Avocado leaves, pits, bark and fruit contain a toxin called 'Persin.' While Persin is harmless to humans it has been known to cause breathing difficulties, stomach problems and fluid retention and buildup in the chest. An Avocado's pit is also incredibly dangerous as it will obstruct your Bedlington Terrier's gastrointestinal tract if swallowed.

Grapes and Raisins

Both grapes and raisins have been known to cause

seriously health problems in Bedlington Terriers – such as liver damage and kidney failure! It is not currently known what specific chemical in grapes and raisins is toxic to Bedlington Terriers. It takes as little as a handful of grapes to seriously poison your dog!

Chocolate

While chocolate is viewed as a treat for humans, it is definitely not for dogs. Chocolate contains a chemical called theobromine which is toxic to Bedlington Terriers. Theobromine will cause a dog to vomit and have diarrhea. It also has the potential to cause seizures and long term damage to your pets nervous system and heart! It is important to watch children around your dog as they may, with the best intentions, feed your Bedlington Terrier some of their chocolate.

Coffee and Caffeine

Both coffee and caffeinated products can be fatal if ingested in a high enough quantity. Coffee and caffeine have similar negative effects to chocolate. It causes vomiting, abnormal heart palpitations, seizures and long term damage to the dog's nervous system. It is important to remember that caffeine can be found in a high number of products such as: energy drinks, tea, chocolate, cocoa beans and medicine.

Macadamia Nuts

It can take as little as five macadamia nuts to have a seriously negative effect on your dog's health. The symptoms of macadamia nut poisoning include muscle tremors, vomiting, rapid breathing, rapid heartrate, increase body temperature and signs of general weakness. If macadamia nuts are mixed with chocolate the combination of poisoning will nearly always be fatal.

Xylitol

Xylitol is a sugar based alcohol that can commonly be found in gum, candy, sweet baked goods and other sugar-substitute items. Xylitol causes no apparent harm to humans but is extremely toxic to dogs. Even a small dose of Xylitol can cause seizures, low blood sugar levels, liver failure and even death in Bedlington Terriers!

Yeast

Yeast can be found in basically any dough products (bread, cakes, etc). Yeast will rise and expand in your Bedlington Terrier's stomach in a similar manner to how it rises in bread. A small amount of yeast will cause your dog mild discomfort and to be gassy. However if your dog ingests too much yeast it is likely rupture their stomach lining and intestines! It is important to never feed your dog bread or any other products containing yeast.

Onions, Garlic and Chives

It does not matter what form these produces are in (powdered, raw, cooker, dehydrated or mixed with other foods) they are always detrimental to your Bedlington Terrier's health. Onions, garlic and chives contain sulfoxides and disulfides which can cause anemia and damage to your Bedlington Terrier's red blood cells. Onions, garlic and chives also cause vomiting, breathlessness and general weakness in Bedlington Terriers.

Peaches, Pears and Plums

Peaches contain pits that are potentially a choking hazard to dogs. The pits also contain amygdalin which contains a compound made up of cyanide and sugar that degrades into hydrogen cyanide when metabolized. Hydrogen cyanide is incredibly toxic to dogs and will normally lead to death! Pear seeds contain a small amount of arsenic which is likewise dangerous. Plum pits cannot be digested properly and will therefore cause intestinal obstruction which can cause multiple dangerous health issues. It is important to check your backyard for any trees that produce large fruits and seeds. If you find multiple seeds in your dog's waste it is probably best to cut down and remove the tree.

Cooked Bones

There is a common misconception that all bones are good for Bedlington Terriers. While chewing uncooked bones can help improve the strength of your Bedlington Terrier's jaw and provide them with need nutrients, cooked bones are highly dangerous. Cooked bones can easily splinter into sharp, and jagged, pieces. These sharp splinters can tear the lining of your dog's throat or stomach. They will also cause your dog a lot of discomfort as they pass the splintered pieces of bone.

Alcohol

Alcohol has the same effect on a dog's liver and brain as it has on a humans. However the effects of alcohol are greatly amplified on dogs and it therefore takes a lot less alcohol to cause damages – the smaller the dog the greater the effects. A small amount of alcohol can cause vomiting, diarrhea, depression, difficulty breathing, comas and death! Alcohol can obviously be found in beer, liquor and wine but can also been found in some food.

Other Substances to Avoid

The following substances are considered less harmful but should still not be given to your Bedlington Terrier: chewing gum, baby food, apple seeds, corn on the cob, fat trimmings, salmon, tuna, milk and dairy, tobacco, salt, raw meat and raw eggs.

EXTRA THINGS TO CONSIDER

The following sections are extra things to consider that did not fit into any of the above sections.

Vacation

It is likely that you will have a vacation at some point during your Bedlington Terrier's life. It is important to remember that not all vacations will accommodate your pet Bedlington Terrier. It is therefore best practice to try and line up at least 3 people who would be willing to care for your pet Bedlington Terrier while you are away, before even purchasing a Bedlington Terrier. Some pet care stores provide a care service for owners while they are on holiday so it is also advisable to ask your local pet store if they offer this service. Another alternative is kennels and boarding services.

Pack Animals

Dogs are pack animals and enjoy being social with humans, other animals and other Bedlington Terriers. If you are going to be away from home for long periods of time (for example at work) it is considered best practice to purchase more than one Bedlington Terrier. It is important that your Bedlington Terrier does not feel lonely as this will lead to depression and unnecessary stress.

Begging

If your Bedlington Terrier begs for food at the table, you are not alone! Begging can seem cute at first but can quickly become an annoying habit. If begging goes unchecked it can escalate into whining during meal times, jumping up onto the table and ever stealing food off plates. The best way to avoid begging is to NEVER allow anyone to feed your Bedlington Terrier from the table in the first place. However if you have already fed your dog from the table I recommend ignoring your dog's begging. Once your pet realizes that begging is a futile process they will quickly stop it. Rewarding your dog when it is away from the table, during mealtimes, is the best way to encourage it to stop begging.

Introducing a New Baby to your Dog

Dogs can become jealous. Jealousy can happen in any breed. All breeds, from Rottweilers to Pugs, have been known to bite or attack babies out of pure jealousy. The best way to make sure that your Bedlington Terrier does not become jealous is to keep to your established care routine. Do not forget to feed, walk, bathe, train and play with your Bedlington Terrier! The first way to introduce your new baby to your

Bedlington Terrier is to introduce its scent. Bring your Bedlington Terrier an item that has your baby's scent on it (such as an item of clothing) and allow your dog to become familiar with the scent. You need to make it clear that your dog needs your permission to sniff the item – this will create clear boundaries and create respect for the baby. Before introducing your Bedlington Terrier to the baby it is considered best practice to take your Bedlington Terrier for a long walk to drain it of any excess energy. It is important to make sure that the baby, the Bedlington Terrier and yourself remain calm during the introduction. Introduce your Bedlington Terrier at a distance and over time (weeks) allow it to come closer and closer to the baby. By introducing the baby slowly you are allowing your Bedlington Terrier to know that it is worthy of its respect. Most dogs have no issues with new babies! However if you are not 100% confident with the safety of your baby I recommend rehoming your dog. The safety of your baby and dog are the greatest priority (dogs that attack a baby are normally euthanized)!

Location

It is important to consider where you will be living with your new dog. If you are going to be living in a small apartment, or a house without a garden, it may be a good idea to consider purchasing a smaller breed of dog.

Likewise, it is important to consider if you neighbors will be bothered by the sound of your dog barking. It may be worthwhile purchasing a breed that is known to be more silent! As a dog owner you will have to ensure that you and your dog have a suitable place to live.

Dogs After a Death

Death is a natural part of life, but that does not make it any less painful. As previously mentioned, dogs have a unique ability to sooth people and empathize with them. This makes the purchase of a dog great for anyone who has experienced a death in their family. This is a piece of anecdotal evidence that I think emphasizes my point. After the death of my girlfriend's Granddad, her Grandmother was understandably distraught. She stopped going out as much and my girlfriend's family worried this could lead to illness. They decided to purchase her a Golden Retriever and I can safely say it has changed her life for the better. By owning a dog, it gave her a reason to get up in the morning, to get out of the house and it also gave her company in her home. Her Golden Retriever helped to ease the loneliness and sadness that comes after an impactful loss. If you, or someone in your family, has gone through a loss it may be worth considering getting a dog to help ease the pain. Another reason purchasing a dog from someone who has experienced a loss is the fact that people will talk to them while they are walking their dog. Dog owners get stopped and chatted to on a regular basis and this can definitely help ease the pain of a loss.

The Death of a Dog

While this section is mainly applicable to families who have children, I think it is important for any dog owner to consider. When a dear family pet passes away it will always cause sadness and an 'emptiness' in a household. The best way to ease the pain of your pet's passing is to remove all of their bowls, dog beds and toys into an out of the way storage area. This will stop you, and your family, being constantly reminded by the absence. If you have small children it may be a good idea to purchase them a cuddly stuffed dog toy, of the same breed as your deceased dog. This can help to ease the transition period after the death. There is no right or wrong way to process the pain of a loss but there are definitely some things to avoid. If you are planning on introducing a new dog to your household it is important to not think of the new dog as a 'replacement.' To view a new animal as a replacement for an old animal is to disregard the individual personality of the new dog. Each dog is different in their own way and a new dog will not necessarily be interested in the activities, manner of petting and the food your previous dog enjoyed. The new dog may process affection differently and it may take time to adjust. I suggest not rushing into introducing a new dog into your family to avoid this.

FINAL THOUGHTS

Thank you for purchasing our pet care manual on caring for a Bedlington Terrier. I hope you have found the information both interesting and informative. I hope that this book has allowed you to make an informed choice on whether owning a Bedlington Terrier suits you and if so I hope that the information will help you to provide the best quality care for your pet Bedlington Terrier.

I will be publishing multiple other dog care manuals on our author page on Kindle. If you have an interest in learning more about specific dog breeds then I highly suggest you check out our other work.

I am passionate about providing the best quality information to our customers. I would highly appreciate any feedback, or reviews, you could leave us on our Kindle page to allow us to help create the best possible pet care products available on the market.

? Heartworms.

Printed in Great Britain
by Amazon

39172030R00069